The Problem of Homosexuality

THE PROBLEM OF HOMOSEXUALITY

by Charles Berg, M.D.

and Clifford Allen, M.D.

THE CITADEL PRESS   ·   NEW YORK

On December 12, 1957, Dr. Charles Berg died at his home in London. He had just sent off the final chapters of this book to The Citadel Press, and it is indeed sad that the work must appear posthumously.

The idea for the present book emerged during a conversation with Dr. Berg in London during the fall of 1956. From that time until his death, Dr. Berg followed the progress of the project with the keenest interest, working closely with his collaborator Dr. Clifford Allen.

Dr. Berg's death removes from the scene a world-famous psychiatrist who had already made outstanding contributions to the understanding of human behavior in his previously published books.

In this book every aspect of the problem of homosexuality is dealt with in a compendious and comprehensive manner. There are a large number of clinical cases described in factual detail, together with many excerpts from analytical sessions. The nature, causation and treatment of this particular deviation in sexual behaviour is amply described and discussed. Stress is laid on the fact that homosexuality is essentially a particular *form* which the sexual tendency has taken to express itself, a form which is of course not so fundamental as the tendency itself and therefore should be and is subject to modification and alteration.

The authors are both practising analysts and psychotherapists and therefore are able to draw very largely from their own personal experiences. Nevertheless the records of almost every other analyst and sexologist in this field are referred to and subsumed, so that the data upon which conclusions are based cover practically the whole field of this particular deviation. Moreover, attention is drawn to the fact that although the term "homosexuality" applies specifically to *behaviour*, there exists a homosexual component in all persons, indeed in all living organisms, and that its various indirect (non-sexual) forms of expression have a great deal to do with the cohesion of society.

The first part, written by Dr. Clifford Allen, deals specifically with the nature, causation and treatment of homosexuality. The second part, written by Dr. Charles Berg, presents a general survey of the whole subject, with special references to the psychological or psychopathological foundations of the phenomenon, and an attempt to solve the vexing question of inherited tendencies versus acquired behaviour. At the same time it briefly summarises contributors from world-wide sources and international authorities.

The third part contains a summary and discussion of the recent report of the British Parliamentary Committee on Homosexuality, popularly referred to as the Wolfenden Report, and reveals the difficulty or impossibility of correlating a scientific, medical or psychological phenomenon with the fixed ideas of legal restrictions and controls.

The views of the two authors do not coincide in every particular, but it was felt that the public would benefit from a recognition of the fact that even experts on the subject can still have some differences of opinion.

CHARLES BERG, M.D.
CLIFFORD ALLEN, M.D.

London, England
November, 1957

Contents

The Problem of Homosexuality

HOMOSEXUALITY: ITS NATURE, CAUSATION, AND TREATMENT

by Clifford Allen, M.D.

There are certain subjects, mainly related to sex, which people are reluctant to discuss. When I was a boy, for example, venereal disease was something which was taboo. One was told in whispers, if told at all, that there was something which could be "caught from bad women" which rotted one's interior and which caused one eventually to be dragged screaming and fighting to a mental hospital. There, after an indeterminate time, when it was presumably discovered that nothing further could be done, one was quietly smothered by a pillow and buried out of sight.

Homosexuality until recently was regarded in the same way. This attitude still exists in such institutions as the Lord Chamberlain's Office, which in England censors plays. It is known that it is impossible to persuade the officials to pass a play which discusses homosexuality in a serious manner, although jokes which refer to it are permitted. In English law the penalty for sodomy is equivalent to that given for some cases of murder—a life sentence.

Yet, in spite of this attitude, some homosexuals are obviously not evil persons and often, like Leonardo da Vinci, are very creative. The prudery of the past has broken down, and it is reasonable that we should discuss this condition openly and frankly so that we have some understanding of it.

Homosexuality is, of course, the attraction towards someone of the same sex (from the Greek *homo*, "the same," and not the Latin *homo*, "a man"). A man or woman may be homosexual without ever committing an illegal act and, indeed, many people who are homosexuals pass through life without ever doing anything disapproved of by the law.

It must be admitted that the law, particularly of those countries which have derived their legal systems from England, punishes homosexuality very severely. This has been suggested by D. Stanley-Jones to be derived from the fact that English law comes from Church law to a great extent and the Church took its legal outlook from the Hebrews. He states: "The English law concerning sexual abnormalities and in particular the law on homosexuality or sexual inversion, issues from the conflict between the rival systems of belief of Greece and Palestine, which interfered little with each other while they were separated by the waters of the Levant, but which were brought acutely into opposition when they simultaneously strove for mastery within the walls of Imperial and Papal Rome." He goes on to point out the strict attitude that the ancient Hebrews had towards any form of sexual inversion. Although he does not make the point, the Hebrews appear to have been a splinter group which split off from the Chaldeans (a branch of the Phoenicians) and the Chaldeans had both male and female prostitutes in their temples. They had no objection to homosexuality. When the Hebrews split off they developed a stronger and stronger national spirit and abolished homosexuality as "an abomination in the eyes of the Lord." No doubt the fact that they were a small tribe surrounded by hostile nations and it was tremendously important for them to breed rapidly encouraged them to stamp out anything which interfered with reproduction, such as homosexuality.

It may be for this reason that the story of Sodom and Gomorrah was invented. Now every judge when thundering at some wretched homosexual who is to be sentenced, quotes the fact that the country will deteriorate and become a hotbed of vice, like Sodom and Gomorrah. However, it has recently been shown that Sodom and Gomorrah were probably destroyed by some natural catastrophe such as the explosion of an oil well and that the evidence of homosexuality in their inhabitants was based on a grammatical mistake.

Be all this as it may, the Bible brought the Hebrew traditions into English law and the Americans founded their own laws on the laws they had known in England.

The Continental countries and some of the Scandinavian ones founded their law on those of the Code Napoleon which have a much more lenient attitude towards sexual abnormality.

I would ask the reader to do what Dr. Johnson asked: "Clear your mind of cant," and forget the pronouncements of the pompous, the dicta of the all-wise columnists (who know nothing about it) and the rash statements of those who rush into print, often for personal notoriety or from personal prejudice, and try to understand homosexuality sensibly from the following points of view:

1. Its occurrence
2. Its cause
3. Its social significance
4. Its prevention and treatment

If the reader will do this he will find that he will understand the matter more clearly than before, and be in a position to form an opinion on it without being influenced by emotional bias and unreasonable prejudices.

Homosexuality is not usually appreciated to occur in lower animals, yet it does so. Possibly when it appears in them it is simplified in comparison with human beings but it is a definite homosexual reaction. It is difficult to state the reactions of animals lower than mammals, but in mammals it can be seen to occur. This has led biologists to use such creatures as rats for experiments. For example, Jenkins found that if rats were separated into groups consisting only of their own sex, and no contact between opposite sexes allowed, after a time homosexual behaviour would commence. This increased in proportion to the length of time of segregation. He then found that when homosexual attempts at mating were occurring, if he introduced animals of different sex a certain number of rats would not attempt to copulate with the newcomers, but still tried to mate with those of their own sex. The number of animals affected depended on the length of time of separation.

Such an experiment is very instructive. Homosexuality is believed to be increased by wars, and the segregation of men in the Army and Navy from women for long periods may have something to do with this fact. It may also be of importance in countries where young men are educated away from girls as occurs in the so-called Public Schools in England. The author has seen homosexuality in boys brought up in orphanages where they have had little or no contact with women, but usually the organisers of such places have enough appreciation to provide suitable matrons, who replace the mother and give the child some contact with females.

When we examine the behaviour of monkeys and apes it is clear that they often behave in a homosexual fashion. Zuckerman, who is a great authority on this matter describes their behaviour as follows:

Two animals will be sitting near each other, their heads will turn, their eyes meet, and immediately they may begin to smack their lips. This social response may then be extended by the animals rising, and by one presenting to the other. Then follows more pronounced smacking of the lips, sometimes a rhythmical series of low, deep grunts, and the animals will either groom each other or mount each other, or both. The females of the harem also exhibit homosexual behaviour—one female assuming the attitude of the male in mounting another. Since females of different harems do not come into contact with each other, feminine homosexual behaviour occurs only in harems containing more than one female. Females also assume the male position and mount young males, and on rare occasions adult females have been observed mounting bachelors attached to their harems. (*These animals were not in a state of deprivation, but in a colony of Hamadryas baboons on Monkey Hill in the London Zoological Gardens.*)

Homosexual behaviour has been recorded by other observers, such as Yerkes and Yerkes, in their classic work on the great apes. It is obvious, since nearly all those who have studied the behaviour of monkeys and apes have found it, that animals in this group pass through a stage in which they are attracted to those of the same, as well as the opposite sex. Indeed Yerkes and Yerkes state:

Copulatory play is both varied and frequent in immature animals. Homosexual, heterosexual, exhibitionistic and masturbationary activities occur.

If one tries to summarise the behaviour of monkeys and apes, one can see that they pass through stages. These are:

1.) The stage of immaturity in which the young animal tends to show great diversity of activity, particularly that which is directly or indirectly connected with sexuality. It shows activities which have been described as autoerotic (getting pleasure from itself, as in masturbation) and it also shows frank homosexuality by mutual masturbation and other sexual activities with its own sex. It has been observed that a monkey attempted sodomy.

2.) The second stage in the development of the monkey and ape comes after puberty, when it procures a mate or mates and ceases to fritter away its energy in constant movement. On the contrary it conserves it for food-seeking and sexuality. This may be regarded as the attainment of maturity and adulthood.

By analogy with the monkeys and apes homosexuality is *immaturity* and the adult ape drops it because he finds copulation with the female more enjoyable. *Since man has evolved from the apes, it is not surprising if we find that he retains some residue of his development.*

If homosexuality occurs in monkeys and apes, as we have shown, then we should expect that it might be prevalent in primitive races and in very early historical times.

The oldest records which we possess are cave paintings, such as are to be seen in the caves of Altamira, Lescaux and Cabrarets. A certain number of these show drawings of men with erect penises. The anthropologists tell us that these are symbols of fertility. Yet such drawings might have been made on lavatories in a modern city by homosexuals. I suspect that some at least show homosexual tendencies in palaeolithic (stone age) man.

Be this as it may, primitive tribes even today show homosexual tendencies. Some tolerate or even encourage it; some on the contrary ruthlessly suppress it.

Ford and Beach studied seventy-six societies and found that 49% considered that homosexual behaviour was normal and socially acceptable. The usual form was to allow the male to dress like a woman and vice versa. Sodomy was permitted in males dressed as women in many societies. In some societies the homosexual man was considered to have magical powers. In some the majority or even all the male population practise homosexuality. In others sodomy is part of the puberty rites. It is indeed considered necessary for the health of the growing boy!

In twenty-eight of the seventy-six societies studied by Ford and Beach homosexual behaviour was condemned and disapproved. Children who showed any such tendency were punished. In adults penalties range from ridicule and social condemnation to death.

However, even in societies which condemn homosexuality there must have been some members who had an urge in this direction. If no one had such an urge there would be no need for punishments. It has been well said that no one locks an empty safe.

If homosexuality occurs among modern primitive people, who presumably have retained old customs for, perhaps, thousands of years, what do we find in the history of early literate races (those who have left documents on which we can base some idea of their culture)? We have already pointed out that there was homosexuality among the ancient Chaldeans and Hebrews and that the Hebrews shed this and disapproved of it with the coming of their spirit of nationalism. The Egyptians have a folk tale dating from about 2,000 B.C. which recounts the quarrels between Horus and Seth. The other gods persuaded them to bury the hatchet. The story goes on to say, "And when it was eventide the bed was spread for them, and they twain lay down. And in the night Seth caused his members to become stiff, and he made it go between the loins of

Horus." Bailey believes that this implies the degradation of the unfortunate Horus by treating him like a woman. But such degradation could not have been possible unless Seth was to some degree homosexual. It is definite that the Egyptians (like other ancient people) regarded sodomy as the ultimate humiliation. No doubt in some cases it replaced castration, which made a man physically like a woman, by treating him mentally like one. In any case, Bailey believes that the ancient Egyptians regarded sodomy as morally objectionable.

The Assyrians, who were a cruel race, had stern laws against homosexuality. There are two tablets which date back to the time of Tiglath-Pileser (12th century B.C.), but probably record older laws. They state:

> Tablet A.19. If a seignior (*arvelum*) started a rumour against his neighbour (*tappau*) in private, saying, "People have lain repeatedly with him," or he said in a brawl in the presence of [other] people, "People have lain repeatedly with you: I will prosecute you," since he is not able to prosecute [him] [and] did not prosecute [him], they shall flog the seignior fifty [times] with staves [and] he shall do the work of the king for one full month: they shall castrate him and he shall also pay one talent of lead.
>
> Tablet A. 20. If a seignior lay with his neighbour, when they have prosecuted him [and] convicted him, they shall lie with him [and] turn him into a eunuch. (*Thus the Assyrian punishment was not only the talion punishment (like for like) of sodomising those who committed sodomy but castration also.*)

The Hittite laws may or may not have allowed homosexuality. Our knowledge of them, as Bailey points out, is insufficient to say for certain. There is a tablet which has been taken to mean that it was permitted. Thus:

Tablet 1 ("If a man") 36. If a slave gives the bride-price to a free youth and takes him to dwell in his household as husband no one shall surrender him. (*This has been interpreted as meaning a homosexual union but some beleive that after the word husband "of his daughter" is meant and so no homosexuality is implied.*)

Another statute definitely states disapproval thus:

Tablet ii ("If a vine") 189. If a man sins with a son [it is] an abomination.

The behaviour of the Romans and Greeks has been quoted ad nauseam. As Dr. Stanley-Jones says "The Greeks of the olden days made no problem of this difficult question: homosexuality was accepted as a normal part of the make-up of every adult and provision was made for its enjoyment, not as an undesirable perversion due to obliquity of human nature, but on a basis of honourable friendship between men of the highest repute." The Spartans in particular founded their army on homosexuality, the older soldier taking under his wing the young recruit and educating him and protecting him. The *Satyricon* of Petronius shows the amount of homosexuality among the Romans.

It would be useless to labour the point more. It is evident that some homosexuality occurred in ancient nations and was either tolerated or attempts were made to suppress it. This appears among various primitive tribes at the present time.

One might with reason ask, what does this mean psychologically?

It means this: Urges towards homosexuality are apparently found in all higher mammals, including man. In some pre-literate races these urges are indulged, but in some severely suppressed. This was the case among the races whose early history was recorded and were mainly of bronze age occurrence.

If we suppress an instinctual urge we do so by turning hostility on it. The newly-weaned child hates milk pudding because it is reminiscent of the breast, the reformed alcoholic abuses alcohol in a loud voice because he can only resist it if he hates it. Similarly those nations which have suppressed homosexuality abuse it and hate it, thus revealing an inner longing for it. What do we find regarding homosexuality at the present time amongst the civilised nations?

They also are divided into those nations which disregard homosexuality to a large extent and those which savagely repress it. Now no nation can afford to allow abuse as Hammelmann points out. He summarises the elements which even the most tolerant nation cannot accept. These are:

1. Abuse and defilement of the young and immature.
2. Abuse of weak members of society by exploitation of a position of authority or dependence; force or fraud.
3. Acts of indecency committed in public.
4. Soliciting or importuning.

Hammelmann says:

> Only two of the ten countries of Western Europe which were the subject of this survey possess in their Criminal Codes express provisions which make homosexual behaviour carried out in private among consenting male adults a punishable offence. These two countries are Germany and Norway, and even of these two Norway, despite the express provisions of its Criminal Code does not now in fact institute criminal proceedings against adults for homosexual relations with other adults.

It would seem then that most of the progressive countries in the world are coming to the view that homosexuality is not something for which Draconian punishment is necessary unless it injures the defenseless.

Let us see how much homosexuality is present in civilised human beings. The best known survey is the recent one by Kinsey, Pomeroy and Martin who found that 37% of the males who had passed puberty had had at least one homosexual contact which terminated in orgasm. By the age of thirty-five at least 50% had had homosexual contacts. They found that two-thirds of adolescent American boys who behaved homosexually indulged in mutual handling of the penis, but only 16% used anal or intercrural intercourse. 30% of adult men had had an orgasm as the result of stimulation of the penis by the mouth.

The number of men who remain permanently homosexual is not known with any accuracy, but Havelock Ellis thought some 5%. Others suggest much lower figures and believe that about 2% is more likely. Hirschfeld believed that 2.3% were permanently homosexual and 3.4% were bisexual. Hamilton believed on the basis of a questionnaire from students that 17% had had homosexual contacts.

It should be pointed out that Havelock Ellis believed that at least 50% of homosexual men never gave way to their impulses and had no overt sexual outlet.

The statistics regarding homosexuality in women are not much different. For example, Katherine Davis who investigated 1,200 American women found that 50% had shown some homosexuality. On the other hand, Kinsey and his collaborators found that by the age of forty-five some 28% of women had had a homosexual response, but only 20% had had actual homosexual experience. Hamilton found that twenty-six out of

100 American women had had "intense emotional relations" with other females. Landis and his colleagues found that 273 out of 295 women had had sexual excitement in the form of "crushes" or strong emotional attachments during adolescence.

No special significance is to be drawn from the fact that most of the statistics given here are taken from American authors. Unfortunately other countries have either had insufficient funds or initiative to investigate homosexuality in their populations. Nevertheless the fact that such a large number of people have homosexual experiences, yet manage finally to settle down to a normal heterosexual life, suggests that human beings, like the monkeys and apes, pass through a stage when homosexuality is part of the emotional development, thus supporting Freud's view obtained from different studies.

Whenever a case of homosexuality which involves a number of men comes into court we are invariably treated to judicial admonishments that this is an increasing evil, that it will destroy the nation and that a stern line must be taken to put it down. It is worth while examining these points to see if this is so. Is homosexuality increasing?

In England the official statistics show that sexual offences have increased nearly five times from those in 1938, whereas crime generally has doubled. This is usually taken to show that homosexuality is definitely on the increase. But is this so? It might be argued that the police, finding it much easier to obtain a conviction with homosexuals, have turned their attention from dangerous criminals to the easier cases. Indeed such an action, if it occurs, would tend to prejudice the figures seriously, not only because there would apparently be more homosexuals, but because there would seem to be fewer criminals.

In my professional experience it would seem that in England

we have policemen detailed to watch for and arrest homosexuals; and that then do not hesitate to use threats and promises to obtain convictions, not only of the man they have caught, but of everybody he has been in contact with. The case given by Henry is very similar to many I have encountered in England. I quote it in full because it is particularly valuable.

T., a middle aged man, described as wealthy and socially prominent, returned home with his wife and four children after several months' visit in South America. He had not learned that a vice crusade was in progress and without hesitation he accepted a telephoned invitation to come to the police station for an interview.

On his arrival T. found himself in a room alone with two men in plain clothes who without mention of their position or interest engaged him in friendly conversation. Then one of the men abruptly changed his attitude and turned on T. with, "When did you become one of the boys?" T. protested that he did not know what was meant and the man returned with, "There is no use denying it. We have a sworn statement from a man who accuses you of having had relations with him."

T. is a cultured person with no previous police experience and was unable to cope with the tactics of members of the vice squad. These men reassured him by promising that whatever he might say would be held strictly confidential. T. then acknowledged that as an adolescent he had been made a victim of his music teacher, a man old enough to be his father. T. had had very careful moral training with respect to girls but he had no knowledge of the love affairs between men. He firmly believed that it was wicked to have physical contact with a girl prior to marriage. He did not understand the relationship with his music teacher, but was not greatly troubled as the teacher had a good reputation and had been employed by his own parents. T.'s father had been harsh and domineering and had kept his children in fear of him. As a consequence T. was especially responsive to the tender and affectionate embraces of this gentle music teacher.

T. acknowledged to his inquisitors that he had, on the rare occasions when his wife was away or ill, been unable to resist the men who reminded him of his former music teacher. These relations were always with adults who had had previous experience and were always carried on in private. None of T.'s family or friends had ever had occasion to suspect him.

At the conclusion of the interview one of the inquisitors asked T. if he would mind signing a prepared statement. Still under the impression that he was assisting in an investigation and that what he confessed would be held confidential T. complied by signing. He excused himself and began making preparations to return home. He was then told that he could not return and that he was under arrest.

T. asked if he might telephone his home and one of the vice squad volunteered to do this for him. The message delivered by the detective was that T. "would be a little late for dinner." Actually he was detained in the city jail for five days before he had a hearing. On his request a lawyer was summoned to represent him, but he was told that a lawyer could be of no assistance to him.

On the day following his arrest, the local newspaper listed T. with others who had been arrested on the charge of being "idle, lewd and dissolute" persons. As a matter of fact T. had been a devoted husband and father, his home life was generally acknowledged to have been ideal and he had been recognised as a philanthropic leader in his community.

During his trial one of his lawyers tried to intercede by quoting from an authoritative psychiatrist. He was promptly stopped by the judge with the comment, "It isn't going to do these fellows any good to listen to that rubbish." The lawyer still tried to suggest that some form of medical or social treatment be tried but the judge was unmoved. "Why," the judge exclaimed, "these men are wanton, all of them, young or old, they'd pick up anyone . . . these pleadings that have come to me for these young men have not affected me one iota."

The judge then read his decision. He concluded with the sentence of six months of hard labour in a road camp, and expressed the opinion that this form of treatment might effect reform. Apparently the judge did not take into consideration that many hours of each day these men would probably have little observation and that under these circumstances they would be likely to indulge in the practices for which they were being punished.

After more than two weeks of this publicity the newspaper called attention to the fact that the vice squad had averaged two arrests a day for two weeks, and, since there had been none in the past four days, it asked if the "sensational vice purge" was "bogging down." To this the head of the vice squad responded: "We'll never stop making arrests on this type of charge. At first you have good luck. But after a while the fish are either scared away or get smart."

Nearly a month after the first newspaper notice of the crusade another and more experienced judge expressed his view of the situation. He "realised, as did everyone else, that long terms in the penitentiary, instead of improving these men, turned them into fiends of the worst type. If prison can demolish the moral structure of a normal man, what would its environs do to a degenerate!"

This judge announced that he would instead of prison sentence offer the defendents the alternative of an operation which would result in emasculation. He reported that in the previous year five men had elected this operation and that the results had been "100 per cent perfect." They had lost "the unnatural tendencies that were causing them to commit wretched crimes." Even the ancient Greeks knew that emasculation of adults did not bring about such results.

Eventually thirty men were arrested. The jails were overcrowded, the police and the judges were beginning to realise the serious mistakes they had made. Public spirited citizens were aroused and demanded that the scandalous publicity be stopped. The ardor of the crusaders themselves began to cool and took a sharp decline after the arrest of one of the leading physicians in the city. The newspaper referred to him as a "culprit" and to his arrest as "the most sensational in this city's vice purge." The physician pleaded not guilty and was allowed to return home on bail. He promptly committed suicide. A widow and three children survive.

T. also pleaded not guilty but instead of returning him he was sent to a sanatorium for the treatment of mental patients. There he saw practically no one for two months except for a nurse or a physician who stopped for routine inspection. His friends had been active in the meantime in forming a committee of physicians and scientists who would undertake the medical treatment of these sex variants. The city officials had become so embarrassed by the problem that they gladly accepted the recommendation of this committee. No further arrests were made and it was arranged that all of the men convicted be given suspended sentence and be required to seek medical treatment.

This brilliant account given by a cautious and experienced psychiatrist accords well with the writer's experience in England. Periodically the story repeats itself. The pattern is like this. The police manage to arrest a homosexual, usually because he has been indiscreet in a park or public lavatory. He is thoroughly questioned and told either that it will be worse for him unless he tells everything he knows or that he is in a bad spot, and that the only way he can obtain leniency is by confessing all. The man, often an inexperienced and frightened person, makes a clean breast of his life, tells of his friends with whom he has had sexual experience and so on. All this is taken down and he is persuaded to sign it. Now the police with a list of other homosexual men go to each one and offer the same threats and promises (which are actually forbidden under English law). The men, alarmed by the apparent omniscience of the police who know the minutest facts about them, confess and sign their confessions. This is fatal for them. No accusation based on someone's word alone will stand up in court, but supported by one's confession it will be damning. Thus one constantly hears of cases involving ten, twenty and even thirty or more men. The day this is being written such a case is being heard in the old Roman city of Chester in England.

The writer has had a case, not so spectacular as Dr. Henry's, which shows the police method. A middle-aged engineer who was homosexual met a schoolmaster, who had similar tendencies, in the bar of a London theatre. They struck up a friendship and occasionally the engineer travelled from the Midlands to the town in which his schoolmaster friend worked. There he stayed in a hotel, and occasionally some homosexual practices took place. The schoolmaster bought some harmless photographs from a photographer by post. These photographs were of athletes and not pornographic. However, the photographer *did* sell pornographic studies of nude girls (which would not have attracted a homosexual in any case) and the police discovered it. They arrested the photographer and told him that he would have a heavy sentence unless he told all. He gave them a list of his clients. This included the schoolmaster. They then visited the schoolmaster and said that they knew all about him; it would be the worse for him unless he confessed. The frightened schoolmaster, thinking that they knew of his homosexuality, told of his engineer friend. They then visited the engineer and repeated their maneuvers. He did not know that he could have a lawyer present during his questioning and also made a complete statement.

The two men, schoolmaster and engineer, were tried. In spite of psychiatric evidence that a prison sentence would do more harm than good, they were given the savage sentence of seven years' imprisonment each, and both were ruined forever. Incidently, a sentence of three, seven or even ten years is by no means exceptional in England for homosexual offences. The writer has seen men put on probation, given three years' imprisonment and ten years' imprisonment—all for the same offence!

These cases have been quoted not to describe police methods but to show how those tactics can distort statistics. One needs only a few campaigns and crusades to increase the statistics amazingly.

The police are not always successful, however, and it is interesting to record how a patient foiled them by his very honesty. This was a young professional man who came to the writer for treatment. He had had a difficult childhood and sometimes found life too much for him. When this happened he drank heavily until he was unable to remember exactly what he had been doing. Occasionally he remembered that he had had some sort of homosexual affairs in these sprees and worried that he might get into trouble.

Evidently he had been known to homosexuals in the Midland town where he had worked before coming to London, because one day two policemen came to visit him late in the evening and said that they knew all about him. He was informed that his only chance was to confess all. He told them, truthfully, that he could not do so because he did not know what he did when he was drunk. They insisted that he must know, but he persisted in his denials. This went on for some five hours, until the disconsolate police had to admit defeat. It was apparent that they had the confession of some other man who had had a sexual relationship with the patient. However, they could do nothing with this statement unless it was confirmed by his confession. This he could not give because he did not know what he had done. Had he confessed he would probably have been tried and given some years' imprisonment.

In such circumstances—as those described so ably by Dr. Henry and those encountered in his professional work by the writer, and others—can one possibly pay any attention to the statistics so hopefully purveyed, and so glibly quoted that homosexuality is increasing?

An English lawyer, in an article which contains a number of mis-statements writes "Since there is no evidence of any change in the detection rate for homosexual offences there must have been an increase in homosexuality." Such a statement is mere oratorical persiflage and means nothing. How does he know there has been no change, and what efforts has he made to obtain evidence? Has he questioned the police, the Commissioner and so on? I am sure that he has not.

The probability is that the number of homosexuals in the community fluctuates a little, but very slightly. This is unlikely to be sufficient ever to form a social menace.

There is one other point which needs attention. That is the accusation frequently made that homosexuals commence by being attracted to adults and then degenerate until they interfere with children. Clinical experience indicates that this is not true. This misapprehension serves to salve the conscience of society, but experience shows that men who are attracted to other men rarely, if ever, feel attracted to boys, while men attracted to boys feel no interest in other men and never have done so.

A point rarely touched upon in books on homosexuality but

which I have drawn attention to in my book, *The Sexual Perversions*, is the occurrence of homosexuality in association with other psychological abnormalities. Too often homosexuality is regarded even by medical men, particularly the laboratory worker, as being simply the converse of heterosexuality or normality. This is an over-simplification. It can be associated with such aberrations as sadism. I stated: "The writer has seen homosexual sadists, homosexual masochists, homosexual infanto-exhibitionists (those who expose themselves to young boys), and a curious case of a homosexual undine voyeur—a man who obtained sexual pleasure from watching men urinate in public lavatories and who was twice arrested for suspected 'indecent behaviour' because he loitered in lavatories. All these perversions (and innumerable others) show a lack of development, as, indeed, does mutual masturbation which is the common physical outlet of the homosexual."

It would be futile to give examples of all these innumerable types but one might quote a celebrated case. That of Fritz Haarmann the so-called "Hanover Mass Murderer," who was a homosexual sadist. He killed between thirty and forty youths and sold their flesh for food, in the tragic times following the First World War, in Hanover. (He said "Es können dreisig, es können vierzig sein: ich weiss das nicht." He remembered thirty or even forty, but apparently he had killed so many he could not be sure of more!) Actually the law accused him of killing only twenty-four. There is no doubt that he was homosexual and it was noted that, "The future murderer, almost as soon as he could walk, developed two suggestive characteristics; he loved dressing up and playing at being a girl, and he showed a deep enmity to his father. He loved dolls, and sewing and was never happier than when helping his sisters in the housework; he was bashful and frightened in the company of boys." This product of an unfortunate home served in the Army where he was found to be a "model soldier," but later molested children and was, for a time, in a mental hospital. Later he was imprisoned for theft and given five years' imprisonment. On release he found Germany in confusion following the terrible effects of the blockade. There were innumerable youths wandering about homeless. His mental abnormality made their murder pleasurable, and selling their flesh profitable. What more could one ask for than to enjoy one's perversion and make a profit from it also? Unfortunately for him the police finally discovered his terrible practices and he was tried, found guilty and decapitated.

It is easy to give endless examples of various homosexual types which show the association of homosexuality with other psychological abnormalities. It must be appreciated by the reader that sexual variants of this type are not just the reverse of heterosexuality; but something more complicated which, most psychiatrists will agree, demonstrates some form of immaturity and lack of emotional development. The homosexual is not just a man with a wicked or perverse wish to behave differently from others. He is not someone offered the loveliness of women and by sheer cussedness spurning it: he is ill in much the same way as a dwarf is ill—because he has never developed.

In the past, and even now, many people talk of inborn and acquired homosexuality, facultative homosexuality and so on. Such terms are meaningless and have been invented by those who have not studied the matter clinically. There are five theories which are worth considering regarding the etiology of homosexuality. These are:

1. It is a form of vice.
2. It is a genetic aberration due to inherited and constitutional factors.
3. It is a glandular disease.
4. It is a psychological disorder.
5. It is a combination of any two or more of the preceding.

A FORM OF VICE

A view often advanced is that the homosexual has deliberately turned away from the pleasures of normal sex and is obtaining some secret, and even delicious enjoyment, forbidden to those who follow normal paths. If this were so one would have to accept that it was a form of addiction such as found in those who discover pleasure in alcohol or drugs. This belief persists, despite the fact that we now know that such addictions are themselves the result of psychological illness. Let us for a moment consider this view. If it were true, one would expect to find homosexual activity only among the blasé, the satiated and experienced. This, however, is not so. Young men who have had no sexual experience often seek psychiatric help because they feel attracted to other men. It is true that almost everybody can remember someone of the same sex trying to assault him, or at least making advances to him, but only a small proportion ever respond. Again the homosexual does not obtain any more sexual pleasure than the normal person (or at least there is no evidence that he does), yet he has to go to dangerous lengths in many cases to obtain it.

The most cogent argument against its being a vice which many choose deliberately is the case of the obsessional homosexual who does not wish to be abnormal. He will come to the psychiatrist and with tears beg for help. "For God's sake do something for me, Doctor, I don't want this terrible thing intruding into my life." Does this sound like the vicious criminal who has chosen the primrose path? It sounds to me more like a miserable, unhappy man who is fighting against an unwanted impulse.

Lord Brabazon, in a discussion on homosexuality in the English House of Lords, pointed out that homosexuality does not form a problem for the ordinary man because he does not feel any interest in it. A woman is so desirable, so lovely, so fascinating in her ways and attractive in her body, that homosexuality is incomprehensible to a healthy normal man. No normal man is ever satiated with women and turns to men or boys because they are likely to give him more pleasure.

There is no doubt that homosexuality can be used viciously, but such things as male prostitution are consequences of and not causes for the basic homosexual behaviour, just as female prostitution exists not merely because of the money to be made

by it, but because of some fundamental defect in the character
of the prostitutes.

If homosexuality were a vice, it might be suppressed, if not
entirely cured, by making the penalties for it so severe that it
was not worth indulging in. However, how many cases have
ever been known to have been cured by punishment? The
writer has seen men who have had as many as four sentences
of two years', three years', five years' and seven years' imprisonment and still have appeared before the judge again on
the same charge.

No, the view that homosexuality is due to some voluntary
seeking of vicious pleasure must be discarded. There are other
and deeper causes.

Genetic Aberration

Could homosexuality be an inborn aberration? The theory
is attractive. It is, in fact, often put forward by the homosexuals
themselves: "Why should I be punished? I was born like this.
I can't help what was born in me." Often homosexuals will
claim that from the very earliest memory they have felt attracted to their own sex and have never felt any interest in
girls. At first sight all this sounds probable. However, on consideration it seems more and more unlikely. If homosexuality
is something inherited it is strange that it is so often mixed with
other abnormalities; sadism, masochism, transvestism, undinism
and all the rest.

Kallman's investigation on homosexual twins is always
quoted regarding this matter. He collected some eighty-five
homosexual men who were each a twin. Of these forty-five
were binovular twins and forty identical twins. (That is to say
the binovular twins were formed by the simultaneous fertiliza-

tion of two ova and the identical twins by the division of one ovum.) The binovular twins showed a 50% homosexuality but the identical twins showed 100%. All the identical twins were therefore homosexual.

Such a study is very difficult. Kallman himself says (in somewhat verbose style):

> Procedurally it is especially impedient in a twin family study of the kind that the road from the point of procuring the name and recorded history of an apparently homosexual twin, subject it to the establishment of a formal acquaintance with the given person or his relatives is an incredibly long, rugged and sometimes perilous one. The subjects are astute in disguising their identities, shifting whereabouts and family connections. They usually live far from their families, and they are rarely able or willing to discuss more than their family histories.

Since the actual clinical data of his paper is very superficial and sketchy and he gives only three case histories because the patients were still subject to New York laws, one feels that the paper, in spite of the elaborate statistical analysis, is dubious and uncertain. Statistical formulas may be impressive, but the basical clinical facts must be completely determined for them to be of any value at all. Obviously one cannot go up to a man and say, "Excuse me, I understand your twin brother is homosexual; do you mind telling me if you are?" It is here that the perilous part comes in and it seems possible that sometimes Kallman went more on hearsay than actual investigation.

However, one statement which he made is valuable, that is: "The axis around which the organisation of personality and sex function takes place is so easily dislocated that the attainment of maturational balance may be disarranged at different developmental stages and by a variety of disturbing mechanisms." No one will disagree with that.

One feels that Kallman's work is too good to be true. The writer has seen at least one set of identical twins in which one was homosexual and one normal. Lange has published a case of identical twins showing similar disparity. West also claims to have seen identical twins, one of whom was homosexual and one normal.

Kallman's paper therefore stands suspect because (1) his clinical material is not satisfactory; (2) it is contradicted by the experience of others; (3) it is unusual in medicine to obtain 100% results and one usually encounters some omission or contradiction; and (4) his work has never been confirmed by anyone else.

Much more painstaking and worthy of study, although negative in their results, are the facts obtained by Lange. He believed that inverts were really genetic females whose physique had shown a physical reversal in the direction of masculinity. This is only a scientific way of stating the layman's theory that homosexuality is "a feminine soul in a masculine body." He investigated the family background of 1,517 male homosexuals whose names were kindly provided for him by the German police. He discovered that there were 2,354 brothers and only 2,034 sisters which gives a male:female ratio of 124 to 100. The normal male:female ratio for the whole population was 106 to 100. It therefore looked as if there might be something in the theory. He believed that the factor which caused homosexuality was transmitted by the father. The children begotten by homosexuals were therefore examined to see if the same ratio persisted. The ratio in them was found to be 106.9 to 100. It is obvious therefore that the theory falls to the ground.

Indeed, investigators have failed to confirm his facts in other countries. For example, Darke in America found no significance in the male:female ratio in the homosexuals he investigated.

In view of the complete failure to prove that there is any significant hereditary factor we can discard the genetic factor. In any case it carries with it all sorts of problems which are difficult to coordinate with inheritance. Since homosexuals tend not to marry and tend to have fewer children than other people, if the supposed inherited factor is a dominant characteristic it would rapidly die out. If it is a recessive, as is usually supposed, it might persist. But as we have pointed out, homosexuality is not just a single factor, such as blue eyes or black hair; it is a number of reactions which can be combined to cause such behaviour as homosexual sadism, homosexual exhibitionism, etc. If there is an inherited factor (which we cannot believe), there must be a whole bevy of genes at work, all associated with normal physiques. This makes it so fantastic as to be unbelievable. The only people who take such an hypothesis seriously are those who have never had any clinical experience at all. Moreover, the fact that homosexuals are often curable by psychotherapy completely destroys the validity of the theory of heredity.

GLANDULAR DISEASE

The view that homosexuality is due to a disease of the glands is an attractive one, although one difficult to sustain. The laboratory is inclined to argue that here we have a male behaving in a feminine way (actually we have suggested that this is not the case, but it appears so to a superficial examination). He therefore feels that such feminine behaviour *must* be caused by some excess of feminine hormone circulating in the male. This view is a perennial one; for instance, in a recent leading article the editor of a medical journal states:

> For our part we are reluctant to believe that there is no organic aberration. When we consider the tremendous compulsion which must lie behind this perverted impulse to drive these individuals onwards in defiance of the savage penalties which lie in wait for them, to say nothing of the attendant personal disgrace, and when we remember that they are often men of great intelligence and ability, of sound judgment, and, outside their perversion, of the highest character, it is impossible to believe that they are not victims of some freakish alteration in that obscure but compelling chemistry that plays so large, if unsuspected, a part in shaping our personalities and destinies.

We appreciate the author's feelings, but surely psychological compulsions are often of similar urgency and prepotency as any endocrine ones.

When the sexual hormones (androgens, testosterone, estrogens and so on) were discovered, tests were rapidly developed to estimate the amount present in the urine. The endocrinologists rushed in and, unwisely publishing papers on what they thought they had found, proclaimed that there was a hormone imbalance.

Wright, Bauer, Neustadt and Myerson and many others attempted to find the basic hormonic dysphasia supposed to occur with homosexuality.

At first, as usually happens, the reports were all optimistic, but soon they were contradicted. Kinsey showed that their results were unsound and that statistically the standard errors in their small numbers of cases were too great to be conclusive. Then that their technique was faulty, and finally that their methods of sampling led to wrong conclusions.

Rosenweig and Hoskins published a paper which demonstrated the ineffectiveness of glandular treatment in homosexuality, and others have confirmed this.

All this sound and fury signifies nothing. It might have been deduced without any endocrine tests from the fact that castration does not make a man homosexual, nor does it cure a homosexual to castrate him. The injection of male hormones in a deviant may actually increase his perverse sexual behaviour and not make him more male.

Hirschfeld's insistence on the physical intersexuality of the homosexual has been proved untrue and his deductions unreliable.

In general, the statement I made ten years ago in my book *The Sexual Perversions and Abnormalities*, still holds true and is unlikely to be disproved. This is that *"We can state with confidence that there is no discernible difference between the physique of the homosexual and heterosexual by any tests, microscopical, macroscopical, biochemical, or endocrine of which we are aware at present."*

It is true that occasionally homosexuals are discovered with an undescended testicle, mild eunochoidism, or some other glandular abnormality, but in the experience of the writer these occur just as frequently in men whose sexual reactions are perfectly normal.

In spite of this, we must admit in all honesty that a diminished endocrine equipment can have some effect and leads to immaturity in as much as it does not provide the sexual urge, and so the sufferer does not obtain the psychological sexual experience necessary for his development. It is, however, a very ancillary factor and may be regarded as "lack of gasoline in the tank." The motive power must not be confused with the route taken by the driver.

Wortis states that he believes that some homosexuals look effeminate because they wish to look like women, but there is no physical difference. The whole problem would be simplified if we could find such a difference and cure it by a few injections, but those who think this have not had enough experience to test their beliefs.

A well-known English endocrinologist has recently insisted that there is no discoverable endocrine abnormality in homosexuality and others are coming around to the same point of view. He says, "There is no convincing evidence that human homosexuality is dependent on hormonal aberrations."

PSYCHOLOGICAL DISORDER

The view that homosexuality is a psychological disorder accords better with the facts than any other theory. Firstly we have the behaviour of the monkeys and apes, who pass through a stage before maturity in which they show homosexual activity. One might expect something similar in human beings. Such a similarity is found in the behaviour of savages, many of whom have homosexual customs. Harrison says of the Big Nambas of Malekula in the New Hebrides:

> The first thing which one notices among the Big Nambas is the way the men go around behind the boys and the boys are fond servants of the men. This homosexuality system is ancient, with its own technique and nomenclature, relationship regulations as to which boys you may like. Each man has his boy, if he can get one; he guards him more jealously than

his female wife. The two often grow very fond of each other. Men who have boys have one or more wives and children. There are more children per head in this area than any other part of Malekula. The women have a parallel pleasure system.

In such circumstances it is not surprising to find, as Freud did, that in civilised human beings there is not immediate heterosexuality, but that the child passes through a stage corresponding to that of the immature ape and characterized by homosexual (and other) reactions.

Moreover, we might expect that if men (and women) are cut off from every heterosexual outlet they regress to the former stage and find some abnormal—usually homosexual—way of releasing their feelings. This is best shown in prisons, internment camps, and isolated Army service where men are unable even to see women. If homosexuality does not break out overtly (and it usually does), it appears disguised under the aspect of men dressing as women in concerts and plays and so on.

It seems from clinical experience that the child needs a proper family relationship, with an affectionate father and mother, and (preferably) brothers and sisters, who do not interfere, but let him develop in a stable, assured atmosphere, in order to attain proper emotional maturity.

Homosexuality is probably produced in a number of different ways but mainly in at least four. We deal with homosexuality in the male because it is more clear-cut and apparent. These are:

1. Hostility to the mother.
2. Excessive affection for the mother.
3. Hostility to the father.
4. Affection for the father when the father himself does not show sufficient heterosexual traits; introjection of an abnormal father.

Hostility for the Mother

I believe that affection for the mother forms a psychological bridge which enables the boy to learn to love other women. If he never learns to love his mother (and he will not do unless she, herself, shows him sufficient affection), he cannot have a normal relationship with girls. Since he tends to shun and detest women, such a man only too often drifts into an affair with another man and, obtaining sexual satisfaction, becomes permanently conditioned to homosexuality. A mother surrogate will, of course, suffice to prevent this.

Excessive Affection for the Mother

This is only one side of the Oedipus complex. Nevertheless, it often occurs when the father is too self-effacing or too much of a nonentity to arouse the full force of hostility which

46

would justify one calling the situation an Oedipus situation. I remember well a case in which a mother brought her son up in a feminine way. His father was a virile farmer, who took little part in the boy's upbringing and the mother did more or less as she wished. The boy did not go to school but had governesses until he was grown up. He was then sent to a ballet school and taught dancing. Naturally with such an upbringing he never developed a masculine personality and had nothing in common with his father. Such a background is common among homosexuals.

The overbearing mother who displaces her husband is a frequent cause. The other things one frequently finds are the father who is not interested in his son, or too interested in his business to give him any of his time. The result is that the boy does not mould his personality on his father and never "learns to be a man" from contact with him. Later on when the boy has grown up homosexual the father is horrified at him and does not realise, or will not accept, that the result is his own fault.

The sudden appearance of homosexuality after wars—and there *does* seem to be a real, if slight, increase—is due either to the fact that boys are deprived of their fathers at a critical time in their development owing to the fathers being away in service, and, of course, to young men being stationed far away from females and having no normal sexual outlet. Not all boys whose fathers have been away become homosexuals. Naturally, some boys find a suitable male, a kindly schoolmaster or uncle, on whom they can mould their personalities and become masculine.

One must insist that to grow up normally a boy must have a suitable man from whom he can learn normal reactions. The boy normally moulds his personality on his mother during the first few years of his life but then should unconsciously and even consciously copy his father. If he has no father, or his father is overshadowed by his mother he cannot do so. There is a possibility that in countries where facility for divorce leads to broken homes the homosexuality rate becomes higher. This may explain Kinsey's high figures but such an hypothesis is not proved.

Hostility to the Father

The same factor is at work here—the failure of the boy to mould himself on his father—as we find in the previous causation. It is, of course, the other side of the Oedipus complex. In cases of homosexuality one often finds that the father has been alcoholic, brutal, intolerant, and overbearing. The boy is repelled by such a monster and turns his affection on to his mother. He feels that masculinity, in contrast with the gentleness and kindness of femininity, is brutal and horrible. This is, of course, not a conscious choice, but largely unconscious. There are conscious feelings also, and the boy often makes a decision that whatever happens he will never be like his father. He has no wish to be a man. He cannot correct his defect by finding some suitable kindly man because he hates all men from the start. Not all homosexuals have such a background, but in the writer's experience it is more common among them than among normally sexed men. The writer's experience is confirmed by Mackworth.

Excessive Affection for an Insufficiently-sexed Father

Here we have not a brutal, cruel father but one who is himself somewhat feminine. The boy absorbs his personality *in toto* and so cannot develop a strongly masculine personality, because his mould is itself defective. This is the danger of the homosexual schoolmaster. Often boys hero-worship school-masters and when they have no father, or their father is not suitable, mould their personalities on that of the schoolmaster. This is perfectly satisfactory when the schoolmaster is a normal man, but if he is admirable in other ways (if he plays games well and is a likeable person) but homosexual, there is the danger that the boys will model themselves on him and so absorb his abnormality without realising that they are doing so. The schoolmaster who seduces boys adds to the menace.

The Love Object

In homosexuality not only does the patient identify himself with the mother (and turns away from the father) in most cases, but it is not generally realised that he tends to regard other men as symbolising a mother in some manner. Various parts of the mother become metamorphosed into the male. Thus the breast becomes equated with the penis, and this explains the frequent fellatio (use of the mouth). Similarly the buttocks become equated with the breasts and is why some men are attracted to tight trousers because the buttocks under the cloth look like a woman's breasts. The vagina becomes symbolised by the anus or mouth. Anal intercourse is only unconscious incestuous behaviour, although it has undergone considerable transformation. The following diagram illustrates the transmutations better than descriptions.

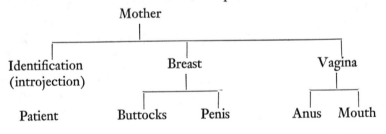

Mother

Identification (introjection) — Breast — Vagina

Patient — Buttocks — Penis — Anus — Mouth

THE IMMATURE LOVE OBJECT

The descriptions given above do not explain completely why some men are attracted to young boys. Clinically one finds that the boy is chosen because: (1) His very immaturity is a denial of adult sexuality. The homosexual man who chooses boys is unable to face the thought of a nubile woman because all the prohibitions of incestuous attraction are centered on her. She is forbidden fruit and he cannot face it. (2) The boy sometimes represents the homosexual as he was himself many years before. Either he is seeking some sexual satisfaction which he obtained at that time or trying to give the boy something he wanted. The writer once treated a schoolmaster whose father had been, himself, a schoolmaster of the most brutal, strict, and unpleasant type. The wretched patient had a miserable childhood and youth because of his father. The result was that he not only became homosexual, but was attracted to boys. Sex did not play much part in his relationships because he felt it was forbidden by religion. On the other hand he would take out boys and spend small fortunes on them, treating them to ice-cream, taking them for rides in his car, taking them to movies and plays, and so on. He gave them expensive presents and treats. All this was not to buy their sexual favors, but to give them what his father never gave him—happiness and affection. Such a thing may sound absurd, but it was certainly true in his case.

How far sexual assault results in homosexuality it is difficult to say. Doshay (quoted by Ahrenfeldt) found that among 108 unselected cases of children between the ages of seven and sixteen who had been involved in sexual and other delinquencies only 8% committed known sexual offences of a minor kind in

adult life whereas no less than 25% committed non-sexual mis-
conduct. Doshay was of the opinion that sodomy, which was
the most usual sexual offence committed by older men or boys
upon young boys or girls, should not be regarded too seriously.
Out of 256 cases only two revealed deep interest in homosexual
practices. Bender, Blau and Rasmussen have done similar work
on girls which confirms these findings.

It is difficult to deduce much from such work. One does not
know how often the children have been subjected to perverted
behaviour. Probably one assault by an unpleasant stranger will
have little effect unless the child is badly frightened, but con-
tinuous assaults over a long period will have a bad effect, particularly if the person who commits them is liked by the child.
The legal prohibition against assault is a wise one.

COMBINED FACTORS

It is possible, as we have suggested, that homosexuality is
sometimes the result of combined factors. An example of this
can be found when such a thing as double undescended testicles
is in combination with psychological elements in a case of
homosexuality. The undescended testicles have not provided
the sexual urge which would have forced the patient on to
have sexual experience. He has remained shy, too timid to talk
to a girl, and never learned how to approach women and how
to make love to them. Such a man will tend to drift into homosexuality as a substitute for something better. The fact that
some glandular abnormality is only incidental is shown by the
fact that one meets plenty of men who have had testicular
disease or damage, but who have developed normally, although
they may not be able to give a woman children. We can say
with our present knowledge that it is only glandular diseases

which are found in combination with psychological disturbances that are likely to produce homosexuality. However, if factors concerned with the strength of the sexual urge are inherited (and they well may be) they could be important, not by causing a homosexual urge to be inherited (that appears impossible), but by not providing a sufficiently strong heterosexual urge. This is merely speculation, since we do not know and have no means of measuring the inherited factors in the normal sexual urge.

We would insist that the basic cause for homosexuality is a psychological deviation. There is the possibility of subsidiary and ancillary factors, such as endocrine dysphasias, accentuating the psychological deviation, but these do not appear ever to be the prime cause. The psychological basis is confirmed clinically by the response to psychotherapy, and the failure to respond to other measures such as glandular therapy.

The Social Significance of Homosexuality

Possibly the greatest importance of homosexuality is that it causes so much unhappiness. If happiness is of any value (and the writer regards it has having the greatest human importance) then homosexuality should be eliminated by every means in our power.

Firstly there is a great deal of unconscious, or partly conscious homosexuality, which causes impotence in men and frigidity in women. Frequently in such cases one finds that the patient's dreams reveal homosexual inclinations which have never been appreciated. I once treated a woman who had had two children but who was homosexually inclined and fell in love with her maids, so that she spent more time with them than with her husband. Under treatment she suddenly found that she could enjoy sexual intercourse with her husband and attained an orgasm, which she had never done in the ten years of marriage before. She had been frigid but did not appreciate it, and thought that all women felt the same. Not until the homosexuality, which inhibited her normal response, had been cured, did she feel these normal responses. Again, many men find to their horror and misery that they cannot react normally with a woman or, even if they do feel excitement, they cannot get a physical response. Such a condition is often the result of deep-seated unconscious homosexuality. Sometimes it responds to therapy, but treatment is often difficult and must be prolonged.

The conscious, overt homosexual is not usually a happy man. One has only to read the books by homosexuals to appreciate that homosexuality is always a *faute de mieux* (something which replaces something better). For example, Donald Webster Cory's book tells of the fugacious relationships which homosexuals have. Only occasionally can they find permanent relationships, and happy relationships are exceptional.

There is always the danger, as Henry and Gross found, that the homosexual will slowly descend the social scale. These authors divide homosexuals into three classes: (1) Respectable Citizens, (2) Prostitutes, (3) Hoodlums.

Unfortunately, the prostitute and the hoodlum prey on the respectable. The respectable homosexual lives a quiet decent life and, but for his homosexuality, is a good citizen. The prostitute is not only abnormal, but uses his abnormality for his personal profit; and the hoodlum is a bullying blackmailer who entices the respectable homosexual into his power and squeezes him dry. The homosexual only too often lives under the fear of blackmail. He has the constant horror that he will be arrested and forced to face the ordeal of publicity, trial and sentence with corresponding imprisonment.

That this is no unsubstantiated fear is shown by the case of a man I once treated. He was a homosexual with a good position. A hoodlum trapped him and tried to blackmail him. The patient went to the police and had the hoodlum arrested for blackmail. He was tried and sentenced, but unfortunately the patient was noticed in court by a friend of his employer who went straight to him, and told him he had a homosexual on his staff. The patient was discharged from his employment, and never obtained such a good post again.

The prostitute often works with the hoodlum. He entraps

some unsuspecting homosexual and takes him home to his flat. At the right moment the hoodlum bursts in and says that he is the prostitute's father or brother. He states that he is going to the police unless the unsuspecting homosexual pays for the damage he has done. The poor man, caught between the police and the hoodlum, pays up and is often forced to go on paying until he is desparate. Not all homosexuals are of the "sissy" type. (In fact, during the war the writer saw a number of fighter pilots who were homosexuals and could be dangerous if provoked.) The homosexual who is made of tougher stuff may murder the blackmailer to rid himself of his misery, or if he is made of weaker material, commit suicide.

It is obvious that inverts are particularly vulnerable and liable to a pressure difficult to bring on a normal man. It is for this reason that they are rejected for Government service where secret material is used. In any case, the homosexual tends to be an unstable person. Burgess and Maclean, the English diplomats who escaped to Russia, were both homosexually inclined, although Maclean was married.

Apart from the unhappiness which his abnormality gives him, the homosexual tends to suffer from other forms of instability. He often tries to drown his miseries in alcohol, although there are usually deeper reasons for his drinking. The writer has treated a homosexual who has twice had delirium tremens, but who refused to give up drinking, and still takes inordinate amounts of liquor. Alcoholic psychoses are usually characterized by ideas of persecution and sometimes reveal the underlying homosexual wishes.

As well as tending toward alcoholism, homosexuals appear to have more neuroses, psychoses and suicide than normal people. There are no statistics of any value but these are the clinical impressions one has. For example, I treated a young man who was a brilliant musician. He complained of paralysis in his right arm, which prevented his playing runs of notes down the keyboard although he could play them up the keyboard without any difficulty. Now this is, neurologically, nonsense—one uses the same muscles for both exercises. He revealed that he was homosexual, and it developed that he was always somewhat antipathetic to his father, who did not want him to become a musician. Treatment cleared up his neurosis easily, and he was soon playing normally. Unfortunately, he then refused to continue to rid himself of the homosexuality, and he is still homosexual.

Homosexuality is common in schizophrenia—in fact Rosanoff and Orr believe that schizophrenia is chaotic sexuality. The mechanisms which Freud has suggested underlie delusions of persecution appear only too often.

These are the delusions that the patient is being persecuted and that some particular man is controlling a great organisation —such as the Catholics or the Masons—which is in league against him. The persecutor is easily demonstrated to be a man with whom the patient is in love, and the paranoid feelings are a defence against the forbidden desires. Thus a more and more complex psychosis is built up until the thing absorbs the patient's whole life. If anyone is foolish enough to try to analyse such a case, the patient will involve him in his delusions and suggest that he (the analyst) is not himself but some member of the gang who has been substituted for the analyst in order to discover his secrets. This situation is not without danger for analysts and they have been known to have been injured, and even killed by deluded patients.

More dramatic is the violent psychotic fear-state described

by Kempf as "acute homosexual panic." These are brief sudden psychoses in which the patient is overcome by an overwhelming fear and behaves in blind panic. He may run amok, sometimes after shedding his clothes, often armed with a weapon such as a chopper, and strike down anyone who gets in his way. The content of his psychosis may sometimes reveal the psychological basis for his illness.

It may be that most of the psychoses which, with or without drugs, release abnormal behaviour are basically homosexual. How far such conditions as the *latah** of the Malays accords with this it is difficult to say and probably more study is needed before a definite opinion can be given.

It is usually accepted that all forms of schizophrenia appear more frequently in homosexuals than in normal people and, even if schizophrenia is merely due to strain and there is no definite relationship, the added stress of a homosexual life is enough to be causal to some extent.

It is the exception rather than the rule to find a schizophrenic married, and often homosexuality is at the bottom of his celibacy.

A typical case is a patient who has been treated by the writer. He is a young man aged thirty-eight. His family on both sides showed exceptional intellectual brilliance. However, there was also a considerable strain of mental abnormality present. Of those known, an aunt was miserly and behaved strangely; although rich she lived in neglect and dirt, and was finally murdered by a man to whom she refused the money he claimed she owed him. Three cousins had schizophrenia and underwent treatment in mental hospitals. The patient's sister also had mental hospital treatment.

* A neurotic condition, similar to jumping disease.

At about the age of eighteen, after an apparently normal childhood, the patient started to complain of abdominal symptoms, discomfort and constipation. He entered the Army during the war but was discharged as unfit. Then he commenced to get more and more serious schizophrenic symptoms. He was unable to think properly, had vague ideas that people were spying on him and vague hallucinations. He was treated in a mental hospital and finally given insulin shock treatments. These removed his delusions and hallucinations, but left him with a tendency to violence. He was irascible, awkward and socially unacceptable, since one never knew when he would fly into a rage and destroy something. The writer treated him with sedation, and at one time with various endocrines (including stilboestrol) but without much effect. He is strongly homosexual and has been so ever since he was a young man. Women do not interest him and he is never sexually excited by them although on one occasion he appeared to be interested (but the girl was not). He has responded to large doses of tranquilizers (chlorpromazine frenquel and meprobamate) but remains a difficult, awkward and irascible person. He cannot settle down to a homosexual life, because this is contrary to his religious beliefs and upbringing, and he feels frustrated without a sexual outlet. There appears no real solution to his troubles.

The relationship of homosexuality to manic-depression is not so definite, but there does seem a connection. For example, Connor found that 90% of patients with depression who had attempted suicide had an unsatisfactory sexual life due either to (1) weakness of the heterosexual urge or (2) the strength of the homosexual urge or (3) both.

Homosexual murder is common and is usually due to two causes. Firstly, as we have pointed out, because the victim is being blackmailed, and secondly from jealousy. The homosexual, by the very nature of his psychological make-up, his unresolved Oedipus complex and so on, has a great deal of aggression which is usually repressed but which, given suitable circumstances, will burst out into unexpected violence.

East, who had vast experience with criminals, makes the following statement:

> A homosexual experience causing a persistent feeling of guilt may be a precipitating factor of a schizophrenic illness, or a reactive depression. I have recorded the case of a restaurant cook, approaching middle age, who attempted to murder the man who shared his private lodgings. Investigation showed that sexual relations had existed between them, the prisoner being the passive agent. When he discovered that his companion was going to marry their landlady he became anxious, depressed and irritable, and was under medical treatment for these symptoms when he committed the crime in a passion of jealousy and revenge. It is, of course, generally recognised that suicide pacts in members of the same sex are sometimes the result of mental depression due to homosexual entanglement.

This leads us to the subject of suicide. One finds this frequently among homosexuals, from the apparently motiveless suicide to the young man who takes his life just before he is about to be married. This usually causes considerable surprise and bewilderment. Here is a young man, often in a good financial position or even rich, who is engaged to a charming girl, often herself of wealthy parentage, who appears to have everything set for happiness. Then the day before his marriage he is found dead. This unexpected occurrence is due nine times out of ten to the fact that the man is homosexual. He has become engaged not because he loves the girl but because he thinks that marriage will cure him of his abnormality. Then at the last moment he realises that he cannot face it and finds suicide the easier way out.

While dealing with suicide we must touch on the curious ritual suicides which are common in homosexuality. These are those of men who dress themselves up as females, make up their faces with cosmetics, colour their nails with nail polish and so on. Then, seated before a mirror, they commit suicide. No doubt this is one final gesture in which they allow their repressed urges to escape, knowing that after death no one can reproach them.

The transvestite (a person who likes to wear the clothes of the opposite sex and obtains sexual excitement from so doing) has a great deal of homosexuality in his make-up. There are probably in most cases other factors, but the homosexuality appears always present. The writer believes that this may be stated briefly as the patient having moulded his personality on the parent of opposite sex, but not sufficiently to go beyond the clothes. However, some pure homosexuals enjoy dressing as females, and there are even dances and so on which (according to Cory) are called in America "drags." Some transvestites are not homosexual and enjoy normal intercourse. The writer once treated a doctor, a tough, burly, football-playing type of man, who enjoyed dressing up as a female and only obtained sexual pleasure with his wife if he wore female clothes. One might say truly that transvestism shades off from the male who merely likes to wear female clothes, but who is otherwise perfectly masculine, to the man who is completely homosexual and wears feminine clothes to his masquerade balls. I have even seen men who habitually wear female clothes under their suits.

Homosexuality is connected sometimes with crime, apart from the homosexuals' sexual activities, but naturally it is difficult to obtain any statistics regarding it, since usually when a man comes before a court charged with, say, stealing, his sexual life is not revealed. Most books on homosexuality do not refer to this problem, so little can be discovered about it.

Numerous authors from Havelock Ellis to Caprio have stressed the relationship of female homosexuality to prostitution but this is so well-known as hardly to need discussion. Caprio states:

> The prevalence of lesbianism in brothels throughout the world has convinced me that prostitution, as a behavior deviation, attracts to a large extent women who have a very strong latent homosexual component. Through prostitution these women eventually overcome their homosexual repressions.

We do not yet know everything concerning the cause of homosexuality, and so cannot state with absolute certainty exactly how a child should be brought up and educated to avoid the possibility of his becoming abnormal. Surely, however, it is wise to use such knowledge as we have, and avoid the more obvious factors even if there are some which remain unknown.

Firstly, nearly everyone who has written on the psychological elements causing homosexuality believes that an unhappy home is important in its production. We cannot supply happy homes to order, but we can do a certain amount to avoid unhappiness. Society is beginning to be aware of this and the Marriage Guidance Movement does an enormous amount of good. One wonders if there would be such a light-hearted attitude to marriage, particularly when a family is involved, if parents realised that terrible harm could result to the children by their separation. No doubt divorce is necessary and advisable in some circumstances. In such cases the parents should do what they can to supply surrogates, so that the children are not deprived of the stable, affectionate environment they need.

However, it is not necessarily only broken homes which are important. There are many homes where the father and mother "go their own ways" although apparently the union remains intact. The children are sent off to boarding schools so as not to remain a hindrance to the parental activities. The boy rarely sees the father and the girl her mother. This is entirely wrong. The boy must mould his personality on that of his father and "learn to be a man" from contact with him. Similarly, the girl should learn feminine attitudes from her mother. The boy should find reasonable affection in the relationship with his mother (and the girl with her father) so that later on they may be able to have proper feeling to those of the opposite sex.

The psychoanalysts stress the importance of the breast and anus in development. Whether one believes in this or not (and there is a wealth of evidence that their discoveries are true) it is wise to avoid trauma in breast feeding. The love and affection which women instinctively show to children in breast feeding them is right and proper. The child actually needs it and craves for it. When the time comes to wean the baby, it should be done by satiating it, by feeding it from a spoon before it is put to the breast, and not by painting the nipple with aloes or anything of the sort. When the child starts growing teeth it should be given hard food such as zwieback to bite and so work off its instinct to chew. It is unkind to force milk puddings on a child who is trying (by hating them) to overcome its longing for milk.

The child's bowels should not be regarded emotionally and its toilet should be a routine matter which does not create concern. Bowel functions should be treated like any other activity—washing its face for example—and not be a source of maternal anxiety. Constipation should be treated with mild vegetable purgatives and not by enemas or suppositories.

When the child takes an interest in its body it should not be blamed, but its questions answered as completely as it is able to understand. Answers should be given unemotionally but truthfully.

The school is an important matter. The mixed, co-educational school favoured in America is much better than the English schools where the sexes are segregated.

The avoidance of sexual assaults on children by adults is a matter of great importance and it is not wise to let the child enter an environment where this may occur no matter what aura of piety surrounds it.

A schoolmaster, as an excuse for assaulting children, once told me that all boys were homosexual. It is true that boys do pass through such a stage, but the very fact that they have to do so and grow into heterosexual adults, shows how important it is that their progress should not be impeded. To interfere with them at such a critical age must entail some risk, even if we do know exactly how much.

Adolescents are sensitive creatures, and it is cruel as well as foolish to tease them when they make their first tentative approaches towards the opposite sex. Many homosexuals have told me that they were developing normally until their families found that they were attracted to someone. The ridicule, chaffing and ribbing, and sometimes even parental prohibition, which greeted this relationship spoiled the delicious discovery of the opposite sex and determined their future abnormality. No doubt there are some, strongly orientated, who can override such jeering and go their own way. It is not with such strongly heterosexually interested young people with which we are concerned. It is those who have no strong urge, who are easily discouraged and turned aside, that we must help. It is they who need approval, even if it is only the tacit approval of an absence of criticism and ribaldry.

Parents now realise the harmlessness of masturbation, and most people have ceased to regard it, as people did fifty or a hundred years ago, as a "sin against the Holy Ghost," a manifestation of the Devil and what not. We know now that it is more or less universal and is the first harmless outlet of an impulse for which civilisation at that age has no accommodation. It should be disregarded and not repressed.

The type of parent who makes the youth of either sex regard sexuality as prohibited runs the risk of forcing the adolescent to seek abnormal paths. This was well shown by a young man whom I successfully treated. His father was a wealthy snob who told his son that he was not to associate with other than the daughters of the rich set which he frequented. Unfortunately, these girls appeared unattractive to his son. The youth drifted into a homosexual adventure with a man he met casually, and started on a career of perversion. His father then lost his money in a financial crash and died almost immediately. The youth was left to make his own way in the world. He spent the little money he had on a legal training and then discovered the severity of the penalties for his sexual behaviour (he frequented lavatories to pick up men). He came to me for psychotherapy. Fortunately, the prohibitions which his father had forced upon him were easily dispelled and he started to develop normally. By the time he was called into the armed forces at the onset of the recent war, he was having normal intercourse with girls and was heterosexually orientated in his manner, behaviour and sex.

There is no reason why girls should not be encouraged to enhance their beauty by pretty clothes and cosmetics (although in some environments parents frown on such things). If the girl has been properly brought up, she is unlikely to become pregnant (which is the constant fear of over-anxious parents), and it helps her to develop normally to go to dances, ice-skating, beaches and so on. It is the ignorant girl who "gets into trouble," not the girl who has had a frank normal upbringing. But to make girls feel that men are evil, disgusting creatures who will bring terrible disasters on them (which was taught to girls so much a few years ago) is to invite them to turn to their own sex for safety.

Sometimes youths of either sex are placed in environments where homosexuality can be forced on them by those in power. This sometimes occurs in Army service among men, and among women in such environments as hospitals by hospital sisters. Obviously everything should be done to prevent the occurrence of such situations, and any report or complaint from those in such care should be taken very seriously. The young people should be of an age when they are capable of repelling such advances if they have been brought up properly. However, once more, we must consider not the robust healthy heterosexual, but the borderline case of the easily-swayed individual not yet set on the right path.

These things may not prevent homosexuality in every case but their avoidance can do no harm and I believe that they may stop its development in some individuals. Those who put forward the view that homosexuality is inherited can suggest little to ameliorate the situation but if, as I believe, it is a disease due to environment and upbringing, it is only common sense to give the child and youth the best possible chance to grow up normally.

Considering its tremendous social importance, there is a dearth of literature on the treatment of inversion. Plenty has been written on the condition itself, mainly by those who have no clinical experience, but research on treatment has been lacking. There seems to be a reluctance to publish anything about it. It is this feeling, perhaps, which made Henry state in the introduction to his book, "I am grateful for the continued support of the Committee for the study of sex variants, and particularly to the members of the Executive Committee. I know that they appreciate the risk which a physician takes in devoting several years of his life to a work which may be dismissed as unpalatable." It cannot be stated too strongly that it is our work as physicians to cure illness and alleviate human misery; if anyone finds this "unpalatable" and turns away in disgust, then he should work in some other, more elegant, profession.

There is possibly another reason why little has been written on the treatment of this condition, and that is that many psychiatrists still feel doubtful that cures can be effected.

Psycho-sexual diseases were first studied by the German psychiatrists at the end of the nineteenth century before any effective psychotherapy had been developed. Their regard was mainly towards classification, and finding some sort of order in the chaotic conditions which they encountered. Treatment was thought to be hopeless because everything was believed to be the result of degeneration. This produced a therapeutic nihilism, the deadening influence of which still persists until the present time.

It is from this point of view that Havelock Ellis made the statement that he had not "any knowledge of a case of congenital or fixed inversion in which a complete or permanent transformation has been achieved by psycho-analysis or other psychotherapeutic method." It is unfortunate that other psychiatrists have accepted this dictum. It is one which places a premium on ignorance and is surely not a scientific argument. If a case is cured, it is not accepted as being one of "congenital or fixed inversion," but if it is not cured, then it shows that the condition is incurable!

As a matter of fact there are a number of successful cases in the literature: London, Naftaly, Lilienstein, Laforgue, Stekel, Gordon, Serog, Frey, Bircher, Sumbaer and others give accounts of them.

In view of this statement by Havelock Ellis it is worth while pointing out that there are not two types of homosexuality, one "congenital or fixed inversion" and one presumably a superficial or acquired type. It is true that some cases are curable and some cannot be cured. This, surely, is true of nearly all diseases. It is true of cancer, but is anyone so foolish as to say that there are two types of carcinoma (cancer)? Surely not. We say that one disease has commenced too early and progressed too far; that prolonged neglect has prevented it from benefitting from intervention. It is exactly the same with homosexuality. For we insist that (in spite of its social consequence) it is just as much a disease as cancer or hysteria. Social consequences have nothing to do with the matter. Insanity has social consequences, but who denies it is a disease?

I believe, based on clinical experience of over twenty-five years, that all homosexuality is acquired, but that some cases have commenced too early, so that they are not curable. There is no more evidence that homosexuality than, say, prostitution is inherited.

I pointed out in the first edition of my book *seventeen years ago* that cases of sexual abnormality, including homosexuality, were curable by psychotherapy. Experience since has supported this point of view. A short series of cases with their results will be given to substantiate it.

Many people, even qualified physicians, advise homosexuals to marry to cure themselves. *This is not only wrong; it is wicked.* The writer always discourages marriage until the patient is definitely cured—that is, until he is orientated towards women instead of men. *It cannot be too strongly insisted that marriage is not a cure for homosexuality and must never be recommended for it.* People should marry for other reasons than to cure an illness.

SELECTION OF CASES

For the purposes of treatment it is convenient to divide inverts into five common types. These are as follows:

1. The shy, nervous, immature man who is too afraid of women to approach them and who as a result drifts into homosexuality, often with a man of similar character.
2. Homosexuality associated with neurosis.
3. The homosexual in whom inversion is accepted as a part of his personality and who does not wish to change.
4. Homosexuality associated with psychosis.
5. The alcoholic homosexual.

Treatment is only likely to succeed with Types 1 and 2. One must accept that Type 3 is too ill, too grossly deviated and lacks the urge to be cured. Treatment of Type 4 is that of his psychosis by insulin or other methods, and of Type 5 of his alcoholism.

There are other factors to be considered. The patient should be young rather than middle-aged, should be intelligent, and should have a desire to be cured. The less he has put his homosexual urges into practice the better chance of a cure.

METHODS OF TREATMENT

Theoretically treatment consists of (1) explanation and education, (2) manipulation of the enviornment, (3) suggestion (including hypnosis and persuasion), (4) superficial analysis, (5) deep transference analysis, (6) conditioning and (7) sublimation.

Patients of Type 1, like all homosexuals, are immature and have never been able to take the proper steps towards heterosexuality. Usually, though not invariably (as we have pointed out), he comes from an environment where his mother played the more important part in his upbringing. Often the patient is terrified of women and, lacking the male aggressiveness, never makes sufficient contact to overcome his fears.

The patient must be persuaded to suppress his shyness and look upon women as sexual objects. He must be made to realise that he is not irrevocably homosexual, but has drifted into such behaviour *faute de mieux* (lacking a proper outlet). Psychological treatment reveals his difficulties, and this often provides him with sufficient courage to mix socially and approach girls. Dancing is then most valuable and gives him a chance to meet and grow familiar with the opposite sex. In such a way his fears can often be removed (as in Case 1), and he will sometimes make such a spontaneous gesture as kissing a girl after a dance. Once he finds that this can be exciting and enjoyable, he tends to progress further. The French say that "the appetite comes from eating," and this is very true of this type of homosexual. As inhibitions come to the surface they can be attacked and destroyed. Sometimes patients bring up the idea that sex is inherently wicked; they must then be made to realise that it is a natural function. Usually, it will be found that ideas of this sort stem from early unwise parental or religious teaching. One must expect that there will be an occasional lapse at first, but in general patients soon accept that homosexual situations are bad for them and avoid their occurrence.

The desirability of women should be held before the patient, but it is unwise to encourage him to visit a prostitute. This is likely to disgust him before he starts. It must be remembered that his sexuality is already at a low ebb and is easily damaged. If he is disgusted by an unsuitable experience he is likely to reject the whole thing as horrible. On the other hand, it is surprising how often he will discover for himself, if left alone, that sex can be a happy experience. Case 8 described below was an exception to the rule, and, fortunately, responded favourably to his experience.

Homosexuality associated with neurosis is the other hopeful type. Even if the patient has no strong urge to be cured of his abnormal sexuality, he has often a powerful desire to be rid of his painful symptoms. The appreciation that they are linked together makes him more likely to co-operate. Sometimes it is not necessary to concentrate on the homosexuality, but to make the patient feel one is curing his neurosis. For example, Sullivan describes a case in which a man was homosexual and had treatment not for his abnormality, but because he lost one job after another owing to incompatibility with his employers. He states, "In the process of studying his difficulties with his bosses, the great homosexual problem sort of caved in." This is not an unusual event, and in any case it does no harm to persuade the patient to move in an environment which favours it during treatment.

Unfortunately, there is no guarantee that this will happen. I have already mentioned a musician with hysterical paralysis of the arm whose paralysis I cured. But the patient did not continue long enough to get rid of the homosexuality.

With homosexual patients treatment will vary from superficial analysis to deep transference analysis taking a year or more. Those who complain that this is tedious and lasts such a long time should consider the waste of years when a patient is imprisoned (*and he comes out just as ill, or worse, than he goes in!*)

Analytical therapy no matter of what type does not differ from that used for any other neurosis. It is, however, in my experience, wise to keep up a gentle pressure in the direction of heterosexual behaviour. This is shown in Case 2, in which the patient had had prolonged psychotherapy under another psychiatrist, but had not been pressed towards any form of sexual activity. When he was persuaded that he must mix with women, he rapidly became normally orientated.

It is, perhaps, worth while pointing out here that neither homosexuality nor any other psychosexual abnormality (except rare cases with adreno-genital virilism in women) respond to endocrine therapy, no matter how dysphasic the hormones may appear. (The adreno-genital cases are produced mainly by the inhibition of the glands and can sometimes be cured by operation, as I showed many years ago). In fact, as I have pointed out, *to give a male homosexual testosterone may make him more homosexual.* The treatment of homosexuals with marked endoctrine disability is not an easy one. The patient must be at least partially orientated in the right direction before given endocrines. It is best for the psychiatrist treating him to have control of the hormone treatment while giving psychotherapy, since he will then know when and how much to accentuate his drive. Nothing is to be more deprecated than casually giving hormones in the hope that even if they do no good they will do no harm. They *may* do harm by accentuating the patient's urges in the wrong direction! In any case, every time the patient tries a new treatment and it fails he becomes more despondent and hopeless. He feels more and more that nothing can cure him.

The use of "chemical castration" by giving female hormones is an expression of despair. It means that one has given up hope of making the patient a normal person. Moreover, it is not always successful—the writer has given evidence in the case of a schoolmaster who had been given enormous doses of stilboestrol and estrogens, but, in spite of the fact that he had enlarged breasts (gynaecomasia) and atrophy of the testicles and penis, he still assaulted some of his pupils and was sent to prison for the fourth time.

Chemical castration is permissable only in men over fifty years of age in whom there is no hope of psychological cure. In them it can be used to destroy their sexual urge and give them mental peace, but even so they should not be allowed to continue occupations which put them in the path of temptation.

Religious conversion has sometimes been cited as a form of cure. In my experience it is rarely, if ever, successful. Many years ago Gibbon, in a famous chapter in his *Decline and Fall of the Roman Empire*, pointed out that religion was no defence against heterosexuality, and it seems likely that it will be no more efficacious in sexual abnormality. Moreover, even clergymen are offenders.

The great American clinician, Harry Stack Sullivan, strongly supports my views in his posthumous book. He states, with his sturdy common sense:

Then I may learn that the patient has often had sexual relations with a member of his own sex, or *something*. That's
what his problem means to me—just "something." The real
problem which I hope to uncover, to my patient's satisfaction,
and with his clear insight, *is what stands in the way* of him
making the conventional, and therefore comparatively simple,
adjustment which is regarded as normal. In other words I don't
treat any alleged entities such as homosexuality as a developmental mistake, dictated by the culture as subversive behaviour
in those instances in which a patient cannot do what is the
simplest thing to do. Thus I try to find out why he *can't* do the
simplest thing, and in such an investigation may come to solve
the problem.

Further on he says:

Thus when you encounter a person with a "homosexual
problem" (in quotation marks, for homosexuality is only a
name) what counts is what you discover about the person—the
particular terrors, menaces, and risks other people hold for
him.

Here is no nonsense about inborn, genetic or essential
homosexuality, but an appreciation that homosexuals are such
because they are afraid to be anything else. They are unable to
be normal because of forces in their minds beyond their control.

Patients sometimes come to me and beg me to treat them by
hypnosis. As far as I know there is only one case on record in
which a cure was produced by hypnotism. This was recorded
by Milne Bramwell. I give it below:

Case No. 49. In one still more striking case, sent to me by
Sir Victor Horsley, on October 31st 1903, the patient's sexual
instincts from earliest boyhood had been homosexual and unnatural sexual connection had frequently taken place. He mar-

ried hoping that this might cure him, but when I saw him there was complete impotence as far as his wife or any other woman was concerned, during the whole of his life. The attraction of his own sex was a veritable obsession, while the idea of touching his wife was as repugnant as the idea of touching his sister. After prolonged treatment by suggestion, he rid himself of his morbid ideas and his sexual relations with his wife became normal.

This is a remarkable case, but no more so than the ones I will describe later—and analytical methods are safer and surer than hypnosis, in which the basic cause is not removed. I think that if hypnosis were a method of choice more cases would have been recorded in clinical literature, and I have been unable to discover any. Incidentally, the remark in the case history above that the patient found the idea of sex with his wife as repugnant as sex with his sister will be particularly significant to anyone who has treated homosexuality, especially since it was written before psychoanalysis. Perhaps it was a quotation from the patient himself; in any case it was founded on the physician's impression of the patient's feelings.

Following is a short series of cases I collected to present to the Royal Commission on Homosexuality and Prostitution when I gave evidence before it in London recently. Extra cases have been added. I have other cases in my records, but the task of sorting them out from the accumulation of many years of psychiatric work would be monumental.

Apparent Cures

Case 1.

This was a man aged forty who complained that he was afraid of women and attracted to men, with whom he had mutual masturbation. His father had been a severe man who died in 1932. His mother was nervous and died in 1940. There was one sister alive and well. As a child he was timid and not very good academically at school. He was poor at games. His glands appear to have been sluggish and his testicles did not descend until he was fourteen.

After leaving school he entered a University and later worked in his father's business. After three years in this he got into trouble with the police for importuning and was sentenced to six weeks' imprisonment. In 1930 he joined a firm of private bankers and has continued in this ever since. In 1940 he was again arrested for importuning and fined fifty pounds.

On examination he appeared to be a timid man, immature emotionally, but willing to discuss his difficulties. Physical examination revealed no signs of eunochoidism which one might have expected from his history.

The nature of his illness was explained to him and a course of psychotherapy embarked upon. He was encouraged to meet girls socially while having treatment. This helped him to overcome his timidity, and he kissed one, but was not very excited by it.

Then a woman friend who was a matchmaker, managed to help him meet a suitable young lady, and he took this girl out. Suddenly he discovered that she was desirable, fell in love and married. He was happy and he was becoming sexually adjusted to his wife (he had a little prematurity) when, six months after his marriage, he developed coronary thrombosis and died. This was most unfortunate since he had lost all attraction to other men and no doubt would have had a happy married life.

Case 2.

This case was that of a man aged forty. He complained that he fell in love with other men and this led him to indulge in mutual masturbation with them. His father was killed in 1916 when he was two-and-a-half years old. His mother was alive and suffered from arthritis. One brother aged forty-eight was alive and well. The patient's home was not a happy one; there was no parental influence and his mother was much too strict. As a child he was nervous but did well at school by working hard. On leaving he entered the Local Government Board service and had done this ever since.

As a boy aged twelve to thirteen years, he had been attracted to girls, but after puberty he felt uncomfortable with women and, although he felt that he should have contact with girls, was too repressed to try. He said that he used to be horrified at the idea of a woman's body.

When first seen he had been having psychotherapy under another psychiatrist, but had not been persuaded to develop his social life with girls nor to regard them as a sexual object. He was encouraged to renew contact with a girl he had known casually some years previously in his home town. He did so, and was attracted to her. When he made love to her he felt excited. After about a dozen sessions of psychotherapy he said that he had decided to marry. This was discouraged until he found that his attraction to the girl was lasting. His interest in other men disappeared completely, and when last heard of two years after termination of treatment, he was engaged and hoped shortly to marry.

Case 3.

A girl aged twenty-three who stated that she was not sexually attracted to men and was involved in a sexual relationship with another girl who was a cripple. She had applied to an endocrinologist for treatment but no glandular abnormality was discovered. It was remarkable that this young lady resisted men so easily, since she was very pretty and no doubt found plenty of men who wished to be her admirers.

She stated that her home was not a happy one because of a domineering and aggressive father. He was excessively strict and she admitted she was terrified of him. At school she had been a timid girl, and, on leaving, worked in a factory. Her looks attracted men, but she was too frightened to go out with them. Some years before she came to me she had met the crippled girl (who was in no way attractive to men) and formed a sexual relationship with her. However, as time passed she felt that she was getting older and should do something regarding marriage.

Her difficulties were investigated and she was told that she was equating all men with her father. She was expecting men to behave in the domineering way he did. I assured her this was not so, and that most men would be happy to be tender to such a pretty girl. She was encouraged to break off her relationship with the cripple (which was holding her back) and go out with men when asked. This she did, and finally fell in love with a man who was trying to get a divorce from his wife with whom he was not happy. She admitted that she was strongly stirred sexually by his love-making, and would have liked to have had intercourse with him but for her strict moral standards.

Case 4.

This was the case of a man aged thirty-eight who was a compulsive sodomist. He had had some homosexual leanings before the war but these were in a minor degree. During the war he was isolated from normal life in the Western Desert in the North African campaign, and his impulses reached a dangerous degree. He did not indulge them until he returned to England.

His mother was a domineering woman and very spiteful. His father died when he was a child. There was an elder brother who was the apple of his mother's eye. This brother went to an important public school, but the patient could not follow his example because he had a mastoid operation on his ear. For some reason this was held against him in the family. However, he went on to Cambridge on leaving school, and was going to become a publisher when the war started. He met a girl who attracted him and married her before he joined the Army. Unfortunately while he was away, his wife had an affair with another man and involved them in a financial tangle. When the patient returned to England after the war, he had a great deal of worry in straightening out their affairs. He responded to any form of anxiety by the compulsion to find a man and have anal intercourse with him. This caused considerable remorse, and he asked for help to overcome his illness.

He was given deep analysis and responded well. The impulses died down after a time, but he had one or two relapses during treatment (as might be expected) and once became involved with a blackmailer. He was advised to see a lawyer, who dealt with this man satisfactorily. He remained well and wrote three years after cessation of treatment: "Both my wife and I are so much better now and it is really wonderful how our lives have changed."

Case 5.

This was a young man aged twenty-seven. He complained of being attracted to other men but had avoided relations with them for some years. He felt that homosexuality was wrong. In addition to his sexual abnormality, he had a superadded neurosis and found it difficult, even impossible at times, to enjoy social life. He was an only child and his father and mother were becoming senile. As a boy he was overprotected and grew up excessively timid. On leaving school, which he disliked, and where he was unhappy, he entered a Government office and worked as a minor civil servant.

It was necessary to treat him by deep analysis. This revealed that he had an intense dislike for his father, which he rationalised by saying that all the work of the house fell on his mother, who was getting feeble, and that his father refused to move into a centrally-heated flat where things would have been easier. He spent all his week-ends at home, decorating the house and so on, which meant that he had no social life at all. He was completely subservient to his mother.

With psychotherapy he improved and slowly came to take

an interest in girls. Finally he became attracted to a girl who worked in the same office, who was in love with him. This girl was married, but apparently her husband was unsatisfactory and uninterested in her sexually. The patient then carried the friendship further and he invited her to his flat to tea. After a few times he made love to her. She responded and later on he attempted intercourse. At first he was not very potent, but he became normal in time.

When he was last seen some four years ago he was still having relations with this girl, who wished to leave her husband and marry him. He was normal sexually with the girl, but admitted that he had had occasional homosexual dreams, and felt mildly attracted to older men without being tempted to make contacts with them. However, since his heterosexuality was so much stronger than his homosexuality, and he was enjoying normal intercourse, it was felt that this could be regarded as a cure.

Case 6.

This was the case of a man aged thirty-eight, who complained that he felt attracted to young men and boys, but did not indulge in homosexuality because he felt that it was wrong. His father was dead, but had had an important position in both the Government service and in business. His mother was a dominant type although kindly in her manner. The patient had two elder brothers; one unfortunately had developed schizophrenia and was in a mental hospital, but the other was a successful journalist. This brother had married a woman who was sterile and, since for family reasons, it was important that a son be produced to inherit a title, it was essential that the patient marry and have a family.

The patient went to one of the larger public schools and did well. He was intellectually inclined and enjoyed study. On leaving school he taught for a time, but at the onset of war joined the Army, where his ability to use languages was employed in Intelligence. However, he felt frustrated in the Army and finally developed depression. The cause for this was his homosexuality which came into conflict with his strong moral principles. Unfortunately, the Army psychiatrists did not investigate this and merely gave him some E.C.T., which naturally had little effect. On leaving the Army he was sent to me and it was decided to treat his homosexuality by deep analysis.

The patient responded well and cooperated as far as he was able. He made slow but steady progress. Finally he became attracted to a woman who kept house for him and she became his mistress. At first it was impossible for him to complete the sexual act owing to the difficulty in producing an ejaculation. This was investigated and the cause discovered. As a boy he had been told that masturbation was a grave matter, a drop of sperm was worth as much as a pint of blood, etc. As a result of this teaching, although he had handled himself as a boy, he was very careful not to go as far as producing an orgasm. It was explained to him that this was nonsense; that the sexual organs were made to be used; that the body was strengthened by use rather than weakened. Shortly after this, he found that he could have a normal ejaculation.

Six years after the termination of treatment he wrote that he was completely normal. He had a family of three children who were a constant joy to him and his wife. He was obviously very happily married.

Case 7.

This was a particularly difficult case and one which I feel especially happy to have brought to a successful conclusion. It concerned a man aged thirty years who was an officer in the Army. He complained that he had never had any attraction to women, but periodically he had a strong impulse to have anal intercourse with men. Men wearing tight trousers attracted him, and so he was excited by those wearing battle dress. (The English battle dress exposes the buttocks because the man wears a blouse and not a coat.) However, he had always avoided having anything to do sexually with men in his own regiment.

With the exception of a few months' temporary duty near London, he was stationed abroad almost the entire nine years he was under treatment. Since I was able to see him only during his annual leave, treatment was prolonged and complicated.

He gave the usual story of an unfortunate home. His father was a drunken failure and his mother a neurotic obsessed with the bowels. He had an older brother whom he disliked. At school he did well and on leaving worked in an office. The war gave him a chance to escape from this into the Army, where he was promoted, and after the conflict, elected to stay in the Service. He was an over-conscientious officer and took his duties very seriously. He looked after his men efficiently, but his over-scrupulousness made him unpopular with the other officers.

When he first consulted me he had never had anything to do with women, and the idea was distasteful to him. He was afraid that he would finally get into trouble with the police because of his sexual activities. This was not altogether un-founded, since he had had narrow escapes, been swindled and robbed, and caught gonorrhoea in his activities.

At first he did not seem likely to respond, but after the first months' treatment said that he felt less anxious. It was not expected that he would return, but in eleven months' time, he asked for further therapy. He admitted that he had relapsed in that interval. Little by little his homosexual neurosis was broken down. His excitement by tightly clothed buttocks was found to be caused by early memories of the breast, and when these memories were unearthed he no longer felt the buttocks attractive. (We have already noted that this attraction is due to memories of the maternal breast under a tight dress.) He found that he would like to have an interest in girls but was nervous and shy with them. Finally, he started to have a rela-tionship with a girl who had been his brother's mistress. No doubt there were emotional reasons for his choice but this was not discouraged. He then discovered that he was in love with this girl and, since he was potent, married her.

As he progressed sexually he found that the Army inter-ested him less and less; his duties appeared irksome and he clashed with his fellow officers. It was obvious that his inter-est in Army life had been founded, as it so often is, on his homo-sexuality and he was now unsuited for it. He left and entered civilian life. When last heard of, a year after cessation of treat-ment, he was living happily with his wife and appeared to be completely normal.

Case 8.

This case is that of a young man aged nineteen who had been leading a homosexual life with a wealthy American in

London. He had been kept by this man and had been strongly attached to him, so much so that he had had "God Bless America" tattooed on his chest! However, his American protector had departed for the United States and the patient decided to try to become normal. He was not very encouraging to look at, since his hair had been bleached and waved. Nevertheless an attempt was made to help him. It was explained to him that his abnormal sexuality was rooted in his upbringing—he had had an over-indulgent mother and a father who took little interest in him. At school he had been average, but on leaving had worked at various unsatisfactory jobs. Finally he drifted into homosexuality and had met his American friend.

He was seen a few times at the Dreadnought Hospital, but little was hoped for in his case. He wished to go to sea (perhaps this was inspired by the men he met in the waiting room) and asked for a job to be found for him as a steward. This was not encouraged, since there is a certain amount of homosexuality on some ships, particularly among the stewards, and it was felt that this might be a bad environment for him. Finally he pleaded so hard that I felt he might be tried on a small ship, where the temptation was not likely to be great. He was helped to find a post, and this turned out to be fortunate. On the ship there were two stewards who took him under their wing. They pointed out that there were homosexual men on the ship, but they would have nothing to do with that sort of relationship. If he had anything to do with these men he would receive a good thrashing. He was to behave himself and, when the ship came into port, go with them to a brothel as a good sailor should!

This crude psychotherapy apparently worked and he said:

"Do you know, I started to look forward to the times the ship reached port and going ashore with them!"

The writer claims little credit for the success in this case. It is obvious that his mates did more to help him along the right road. When last seen he was leading a heterosexual life.

Case 9.

This was a young boy aged seventeen. He complained that he had had attraction towards other men since puberty and this created feelings of desperation and depression. He had been so depressed by his homosexual urges that he had twice attempted suicide. He was the only son of normal parents; his father had died when he was a child and he had been brought up by his mother. At school he was nervous. On leaving school he worked for a tailoring chain. His sexual life seems to have consisted in desperate struggles against his abnormal sexuality.

He was seen once privately and told to attend the Seamen's Hospital when the transfer to London, which he had requested, and which had been granted by his employers, had been effected. Since then he has attended once at the hospital. He stated that since the one interview he had been able to correct his sexual life and now was able to regard girls from a different point of view. They excited him, and he enjoyed their company. He had had no sexual relations with them but his changed attitude showed that he had become immensely more adult. This case would appear incredible except that a similar change has occurred in a few interviews in others (such as Cases 11 and 12).

Case 10.

This was a young schoolmaster aged thirty-six. He complained of homosexual feelings towards boys about the age of seven to seventeen years. He was also attracted to the thought of masturbation and frequented public lavatories in the hope of seeing someone doing it. There was a neurotic interest in his own health.

His parents had died (his father in 1944 and his mother in 1954). He had two brothers and three half-sisters all alive and well. As a child he was nervous and more attracted to his mother than his father. At his preparatory school he was happy but disliked his public school. He had no school friends. On leaving he took a commercial course, and then worked in an insurance office. He wished to become a musician but could not afford it. Then he was left a legacy which enabled him to go to college. He had wished to become a clergyman, but when he had taken his degree decided to teach. He had been teaching for six years when I first saw him.

His sexual life had been rather negative. He did not masturbate until aged 24 and had had no homosexual adventures. He did not interfere with children because he realised that it was wrong. Girls he found attractive for their beauty but not sexually exciting.

On examination he was found to be somewhat eunochoid and there was little hair on his abdomen. He said that he shaved daily but it would not be noticed if he had not done so.

He was not given testosterone at first because it was not considered wise to stimulate his sexuality until the psyche was normally orientated. However, he responded to superficial psychotherapy. He stated that he was repulsed by breasts (a not uncommon finding) and had a fear of making love to girls. He said that "this came from a sort of atmosphere radiated from my mother." His mother had brought him up to the view that sexual thoughts were impure, and he had had no sexual instruction.

He was encouraged not only to discuss his emotional difficulties but to attend dances and socials where he could meet girls. Soon he lost his interest in boys and was attracted to girls. He went to the trouble of joining a club where he could meet them. He has become very friendly with a girl but, although she was willing, did not have intercourse with her. He is not considered entirely cured because of this and it is hoped he will have further treatment, but he is certainly turned towards girls, and no longer interested in boys as he was formerly. From the medicinal point of view it is interesting to note that he responded much better to a sedative and full doses of strychnine rather than methyl testoserone, which seemed to have little or no effect in spite of his slight glandular dystrophy.

Case 11.

This young man, aged twenty-three, was seen only once. He stated that not only was he attracted by other men but sometimes excited by little girls. He was going out with a nurse but was not very responsive to her. On examination no physical abnormality was discovered.

He came from a family composed of a dour Scots father and a much gentler mother. Not surprisingly, he preferred his mother and had never been able to make any real contact with his father. He stated that he was not nervous as a child, but since he had always bitten his nails this did not appear to be true. At school he was average, but not good at games. On leaving school he did a few odd jobs and then worked as an assistant in a chain grocery store.

At the age of thirteen he had been molested sexually by a man who had shown him how to masturbate. This was a great emotional shock. Afterwards he had never had anything to do with men sexually, but preferred the company of a man friend to that of the young nurse he was friendly with. In spite of this, he had kissed girls but never dared to go farther. When he was seen, it was pointed out that it was essential that he try to develop his personality and that he should regard girls from a more sexual point of view. He understood and agreed with what he was told. It was thought that he might respond to a little extra "magic" so he was given testosterone by mouth. He promised to report progress and if necessary arrange to be transferred to London so that he could have further psychotherapy. It was felt unlikely that much would result without it. However, three months later he wrote to say that he had been following the instructions and was progressing well.

I admit that this is a very slight case, but often such apparently trivial impulses end in confirmed homosexuality.

Case 12.

This young man aged twenty-seven came for treatment because he was attracted to men. He came from a normal family, except that he felt his parents were inclined to be nervous and that his father did not like him. The family was Jewish. He was an only child. As a child he had been "delicate," but had grown up normally. He did well at school, and, on leaving, entered an advertising agency. He had learned masturbation from other boys as a lad and at fifteen he was "touched" by a man. This did not lead to mutual masturbation. But a year later he had an affair with a boy, and this did lead to mutual masturbation. Later, he had another affair and indulged in oral and anal intercourse, from which he obtained pleasure. The man involved with him was deeply attached to him and caused considerable trouble during treatment. He threatened suicide and took aspirins to frighten the patient. However, after three sessions the patient appreciated the cause for his difficulties. He was able to mix freely with girls, and having found one who attracted him, he arranged to go on holiday with her and her parents. They went for a motor tour on the Continent. During this trip he and the girl were able to go to bed together. He was sexually excited, but they did not have intercourse because they wanted to wait until they married. The patient came to see me once more and said that he felt perfectly normal, that he cared a great deal for his fiancée, and had lost all interest in his former male friend. Since he was excited by the girl and loved her, there seemed no reason why they should not marry as they proposed to do.

Case 13.

This case was of a young man aged twenty-eight. He complained that he was attracted to other men. Physically he had poor hair development over the masculine areas (the chest and abdomen), although there was no abnormality clinically in his testicles. He was the only child and had always been attached to his mother. His father was a self-opinionated man who strutted about and ruled the roost at home. As a child, the patient was nervous and wet the bed until the age of ten. At school he did not get on well and was very nervous if anyone supervised him closely while he was working. When he left school his father apprenticed him to engineering (he himself was an engineer), but the patient did not like it and gave it up after a year. He then entered a book-selling organisation and liked the clerical work he did there. He went abroad in 1954, and worked as a missionary for ten months, but broke down and developed a neurosis for which he was advised to return to England. On returning to England, he worked for the same book-selling organisation until he came to me. Before he did so he had had psychotherapy under another psychiatrist, but complained that he had made no progress. This was untrue— he *had* made some improvement. He told various stories of men trying to seduce him and his attraction to them, but his experience had been meagre. He was afraid of women but had found a thirty-eight-year-old woman, who had lodged with his parents, who was attracted to him and helped him. He put forward the defence that his religion would not allow him to have intercourse with a woman until he was married; yet it seemed unlikely that he would ever marry until he developed more sexually.

He had psychotherapy and after eight months noticed that he had developed much more body hair. This is not unusual —Ross has recorded the same thing. He had intercourse with his woman friend and appeared to be perfectly normal in his reactions. The attraction to other men diminished to negligible proportions as his interest grew in regard to the other sex.

Case 14.

This was a young woman aged twenty-four. She complained that she was depressed, could not study, and was homosexually attracted to other girls. Her parents were alive and well. The father was a dour, bad-tempered Scotsman. Her mother was tolerant and motherly. There were two brothers and two sisters. Her home was not a happy one—her father knocked her about and was unbearable. She was in consequence nervous as a child and very shy. At school she did badly but was good at English and needlework. She says she was a failure at the rest. On leaving she was apprenticed to millinery but "got sick of it after a few years." She had left home and was working as a filling station attendant when first seen. Her sexual life had been somewhat confused. In spite of her homosexual feelings she had lived with a young man who kept a bookshop for the past four years. This was not happy and she did not wish to marry and have children. In fact this affair was only a defiance of her father whom she wished to outrage. She was not completely homosexual, since she had obtained satisfaction from her lover, but she dressed in trousers, wore unattractive sweaters, and was grubby and unkempt. She had attractions toward women, but had never had any relations with them. She had had treatment in a mental hospital voluntarily for her sexual difficulties, but had seen the doctors only a few times and no real effort had been made to investigate her case. She had served in the A.T.S. (the women's branch of the British Army), but had become depressed and was medically discharged. She said firmly: "I don't like men as a sex."

Treatment consisted in unearthing the hostility which she

bore to her father. This was not difficult and she was willing to talk freely of his misdeeds (he seems to have been a most unpleasant type) at length. As she improved she commenced to become more feminine. It was amusing to see her slowly swing round, and instead of wearing a dirty, unbecoming sweater, change to a more attractive one, and add little feminine touches, such as a powder blue chiffon scarf. She revealed hostility to her mother for her passivity and for not leaving her father. After this the patient became more feminine in her dress and behaviour. She finally said that she felt perfectly normal and was inclined to marry her lover instead of tolerating him. Her clothes became completely feminine. When last seen she wore a canary yellow sweater and a brown corduroy skirt, and used cosmetics. She said that she had no interest in women sexually and was finding a more womanly job than working at a filling station. Her treatment consisted of one weekly session for six months.

SOCIAL CURES

Case 15.

This is the case of a schoolteacher aged fifty-six. He had been in trouble with the police previously for interfering with small boys, and was again in trouble when I saw him in 1954. It was only because treatment was available that he was placed on probation.

His father was a doctor who had died three years before our first session. A deceased brother had been a well-known surgeon. His mother was alive but senile.

The patient had never been on satisfactory terms with his father (who was a Victorian type) and they were antipathetic to each other. At preparatory school he was not happy because he was bullied, but at one of the larger public schools he progressed well and became Head Boy. He served in the First World War and then went to Cambridge, where he took a degree. On leaving, he taught in various schools.

He said that he had never had any sexual instruction, in spite of the father and brother being medical men, and that his sexual feeling was first aroused by a picture in a book of a boy running to rescue another boy who was tied up. After this, he had a strong desire to be tied up or to tie up other boys. While at Cambridge, he developed the habit of caning himself and so arousing sexual feeling, which he released by masturbation. At school, he had been masturbated by another boy, and at Cambridge this occurred again. When he was teaching in various schools he molested boys, until he was discovered in 1930 and sentenced to a year's imprisonment. After he served this he taught in further schools until he was again caught just before treatment started.

He realised that his behaviour had been wrong, and went to one of the larger London hospitals before his second offence. Unfortunately, he was interviewed in front of a class of students and this embarrassed him so much that he refused to attend again.

He admitted that for many years he had indulged in homosexuality either by mutual beating or by rubbing powder into the buttocks. He explained this latter by saying that it was "like powdering a baby." There had never been any indulgence in anal intercourse. Women did not attract him, and he would not like one to beat him.

I realised at once that a complete cure was impossible

owing to his age and the severity of his sexual neurosis (sado-masochistic homosexuality with considerable infantile fixations). He cooperated as far as he could and every effort was made to help him (1) to avoid teaching boys and (2) to find some absorbing interest. He was allowed to teach girls (with whom he was perfectly safe), but he found this dull and uninteresting. He coached adults for examinations without much enthusiasm. At one time he considered being converted to Roman Catholicism, but never bothered to take instruction.

Finally he decided to study psychic research. This he has done and finds that paranormal perception and the like sufficiently absorbing to occupy his time. Since he has sufficient private means to indulge in this hobby it has been encouraged. He has remained well for about two years after the termination of treatment and there is every likelihood of his doing so indefinitely.

Case 16.

This was a man aged thirty-seven. He complained that he was not attracted to women and was only interested in other men. There were also a number of anxiety symptoms which troubled him.

His father had been a large farmer and died in 1939. The patient did not get on well with him, and, as at his birth, he was already an oldish man, there was no point of interest between them as he grew up. The mother was a facile, foolish type without much intelligence. One brother, four years older, had died of encephalitis.

The patient as a child was high-strung. His mother had wanted a girl and brought him up as one, directing his in-

terest towards dolls and other feminine toys. At his preparatory school he was not happy, could not get on with the other
boys, and so was taught by governesses. Then, at the age of
nine years, his mother brought him to London, where he was
sent to a well known ballet school. There he was successful and
decided to make dancing his career. On the stage he was sufficiently good to be asked to dance in many theatrical pro-
ductions in the West End of London.

As a boy he had masturbated alone, but later had indulged
in mutual masturbation. This was mainly with other ballet
dancers. He had never been sexually interested in children and
had had no anal intercourse. Women did not attract him and,
although he lived in an environment where heterosexual outlets were easy, he did not take advantage of the opportunities.

During the War he served in the R.A.F. but, as one might
have expected, he was not successful and was finally medically
discharged.

On examination it was found that he was eunuchoid, which
no doubt explained his weak sexual urge. He was very neurotic and complained of various anxiety symptoms. His manner was effeminate, but he was not a vicious person and had
many kindly impulses.

He was given sedation for his neurosis. It was obvious that
he was too ill to respond to psychotherapy and this was not
attempted. However, he was able to discuss his problems sensibly, and was eager to take helpful advice. He wished to avoid
homosexual outlets. Since his career lay in stage work and he
was getting too old to dance it was suggested that he concentrate on singing. This he has done and he has lived satisfactorily for the last two years.

Case 17.

This was a man aged thirty-six who was accused of assaulting three boys. The assault was not a very serious one—he had asked them to beat him and had beaten them, but not enough to hurt them. On examination he was found to be very fat; there was hair only over a female distribution on his body and the skin was feminine in texture. His sexual organs were normal. It was clear that he was suffering from eunuchoidism, probably related to Fröhlich's syndrome.

The writer gave evidence for him, explained that he was physically as well as mentally ill, and he was placed on probation for a year on condition that he have treatment.

His family history was normal—father, mother and two brothers were all alive and well. There was no glandular or nervous illness in the family.

The patient was the youngest son. He had not been nervous as a child, but had always been fat, and this led to bullying at school. On leaving school he worked for various firms, mainly as an engineer, but was not very successful. On one occasion, he lost money because of a dishonest partner. He was rejected for the R.A.F. during the War because of obesity and low blood pressure. Finally, he obtained work as a travelling salesman, and was doing this when arrested.

Sexually he had been retarded. He was shown masturbation at school, but was unable to indulge in it until he was seventeen, when he reached puberty. He had also seen homosexuality at school, but his late puberty prevented any activity of this nature. He stated that he had had intercourse with girls but, although this was satisfactory, he felt weary and worn out after it. He feared that he might impregnate the girl.

He was treated for a year with methyl testosterone by mouth, up to 50 mg. daily, but this had little effect. Nor did he respond to psychotherapy. However, in spite of lack of response to treatment, he had been in no further trouble for the past six years.

Case 18.

This case was that of a man aged forty when first seen. He was a schoolmaster from the Far East who complained that he was sexually attracted to small boys, and had been unable to continue his work for that reason. He had never actually interfered with his pupils, but concentrated on the waifs and strays who are found in the East.

Physically he suffered from an undescended testicle, but there was no evidence of eunuchoidism.

He had been brought up as a child under the influence of a dominant mother and sister. His father died when the patient was young, and there had been little sympathy between them. His mother had had a very strong emotional influence on him and combined forces with his sister to dominate him.

He was first introduced to homosexuality at his public school, but it was very seriously disapproved of there and he managed to suppress it. Then he went to a university and after taking his degree, moved to the Far East. There he taught for many years. At first he had not been troubled by sex, but there were few outlets with white girls, and he had had no real sexual relief for some years. He had tried to have intercourse with Chinese girls, but they did not excite him and he was impotent with them. Finally, during the two years before he came for treatment, he had had strong homosexual emotions.

He cooperated well in treatment and his lively intelligence made this rapid. After a time he managed to acquire women friends, and had successful intercourse with them, but felt that he was too old to marry. He returned to the Far East to continue teaching, but, unfortunately, was given worrying administrative work. This upset him. A year later, he commenced to feel anxious lest he should break down again, and have further homosexual impulses (although he had had none since treatment). He returned home and had further therapy. This resulted in a complete break with his mother, who again tried to dominate him. He has since lived normally and has been successful in a university post which does not bring him into contact with small children. The fact that he fears that he might relapse suggests that he is not completely cured. Had he married contentedly or had no anxiety regarding relapse he would have been considered a complete cure.

FAILURES

Case 19.

This concerned a schoolmaster, aged forty-five, who was charged with interfering with his pupils. He was treated sympathetically by the judge and placed on probation under my care.

He had been the son of an inspector in the police who had treated him harshly as a child. His mother had been more sympathetic. On leaving school where he had been intellectually successful, he became a teacher and had built up a flourishing preparatory school. Unfortunately he could not resist handling his pupils' genitalia and this had finally brought him to the Courts.

He was treated during his probation and cooperated as far as he could, but it was realised from the first that he was too old for psychotherapy, and a social cure was all that could be expected. He was told that he must never again teach boys and agreed that he would never do so. He bought a pig farm, but found that the heavy work was too much for him after fifteen years of sedentary teaching. He sold it and started a girls' school. There was no objection to this since he was unlikely to interfere with female children. The school grew, and a number of influential people in the district sent their little girls to him. Then, unfortunately, he was asked to take some little boys of kindergarten age and was weak enough to accept them. He was unable to resist the temptation which they afforded, relapsed, and was discovered. Finally, he was brought to Court and sentenced.

Case 20.

This was a priest aged twenty-six when first seen in 1946. He was accused of interfering with small boys. He had had an unfortunate family and personal history. His father was a psychopathic drunkard. One of the father's sisters had been certified insane. His mother was unstable and at one period had been insane and confined in a mental hospital. A brother had died of fits.

As a child and young man he had been excessively nervous (possibly as a result of his father's drinking), and in his later 'teens had behaved oddly. On one occasion he took two of his father's ferrets and banged them together until they died. Another time he had stabbed a pillow with a long bread-knife and told his mother that he was "practising" (presumably to stab her).

In spite of this he was a good student and went to Leeds University, where he took a B.A. In 1943 he was ordained a priest. After this he taught in a school where he was not only teacher but Scout-master.

I was allowed to treat him from May to June, 1946, before his case came up for trial. Unfortunately the charge against him was a grave one—he had interfered with more than thirteen different boys—and he was sent to prison for five years. Nothing further was heard of him until he was seen again in 1954. He was again in trouble with the police and likely to be charged.

He appeared unconcerned about this and showed no remorse or guilt. He had taken no precautions against discovery although he had interfered with no less than twenty-eight boys. In general, his manner and behaviour suggested schizophrenia, which might be expected in view of his family history and early environment. He was therefore certified and sent to a private mental hospital. The superintendent there agreed with the diagnosis. In spite of this he was later charged and tried. He was given ten years' imprisonment.

Such a case as this was hopeless from the first, and the opportunity for psychotherapy was far too short to effect anything of use. In any case he never should have been sent to prison. He belonged in a mental hospital.

Case 21.

This was that of a man aged twenty-nine years. He complained of homosexuality with mutual masturbation, depression and indecision. His father had died of heart failure ten years previously. He had got on well with the patient. The mother had died of cerebral hemorrhage a year previously. The patient had got on badly with her. He was an only child. At school (where his parents were schoolteachers) he did well. He spent a year on a farm on leaving school and then entered a veterinary college. There he did well, and qualified with no difficulty.

As a boy he had masturbated, but not worried unduly regarding it. He was never interested in girls, and could not raise any enthusiasm about them. In fact he disliked them. He said that he could not visualise being normally sexed. His sexual outlet was mutual masturbation with other men. This usually occurred after he had been drinking heavily. This was a dangerous tendency and nearly ended in disaster. He had worked as a veterinary assistant in the Midlands, and then obtained an assistantship on the South Coast. One day detectives called on him and started asking him questions regarding his activities in the Midlands. He answered truthfully that he did sometimes go out and get drunk. When this happened he might have had mutual masturbation with other men, but had no recollection of any homosexual adventures because he was too intoxicated to remember. The detectives questioned him for *five hours*, but he stuck to his story (which was true) and in spite of threats, promises, bullying and argument he would not be moved. They eventually retired, defeated.

A considerable amount of psychotherapeutic work was done, but unfortunately his basic hostility to women (founded on his hatred for his over-bearing mother) could not be moved. However, he gave up drinking and dealt satisfactorily with a difficult situation (his employer's wife had fallen in love with him), but could not be cured. He had not had a drink for about six months when last seen nor had he had any sexual relations with either sex. He was still basically homosexual.

His case is interesting because it shows an unusual psychopathology—hostility to the mother and affection to the father —which reflected itself in his sexual behaviour.

Obviously from such a small number of cases no statistical conclusions can be drawn. Nevertheless, these sample cases are typical of others in my long experience with the diagnosis, assessment and treatment of homosexuality. The first point which is suggested is that homosexuality is not inherited but is the result of environment, and that the environmental element most often to blame is an unhappy or broken home. Hostility or over-affection to one of the parents is the usual dominant factor. The death of the parent of the same sex appears also to have a grave import in its production. In childhood the future invert is often timid and shy, if male; and tomboyish if feminine.

A large number of homosexuals are shy, timid persons in adult life and often drift into abnormal relationships with similar men. Some become deviated in early life, and, by the time they are adult, are too ill to respond to treatment. *But even the most grave cases may respond!* (For example, Case 7.)

Homosexuality may be related to, or involved with, other perversions of which sado-masochism is probably the commonest. Such cases do not necessarily provide more difficulty than the others.

It definitely is not true that homosexuality is incurable. *Those who make such statements have never tried to treat it.* I have always insisted that sexual perversions are as treatable and the results as rewarding as the neuroses. The fact that some cases are too severe or have been too long neglected should not discourage us from treating the more suitable ones. Moreover, even those homosexuals who are too old, whose abnormality is too ingrained, and whose personalities are too rigid, may still benefit from treatment such as stilboestrol or, if their perversions are released by such circumstances as anxiety or alcohol, by help in dealing with such trigger factors.

If anyone complains that the apparent cures which I have given are most inadequate I would agree. I would like to treat every patient for an hour a day for five years. Theoretically someone whose life changes after a few interviews is still much the same in his deeper unconscious as he was previously. Yet, it seems to me, that there is the possibility that some minor fixations may hinder the development of an individual much as a speck of dust may block the jet of the carburetor and prevent a car's progressing. Theoretically, I suppose, if one's car stops, one should strip the whole engine down and clean everything meticulously, yet most of us are satisfied by blowing the dust out of the jet, reassembling the carburetor and going on our way. The problem of treatment hinges on all sorts of factors ignored by theoreticians. Most of the patients who come for treatment are young people, often paying more than they can afford, and making great personal sacrifices to get well. As soon as they *feel* well, respond normally to the opposite sex, and perhaps enjoy intercourse, they no longer see the necessity to continue treatment indefinitely to clear away the unconscious factors remaining. Who can insist that they are wrong? Most human beings manage to grow adult and live normally without prolonged psychotherapy and if one told the average man, who had no overt symptoms, that he needed five years' analysis he would be outraged, perhaps justifiably. The only way one can tell if a person is sexually normal, surely, is that he behaves normally, appears normal, and enjoys a happy sexual life. If he has been abnormal in the past and one can help him to attain that state, it does not seem to me to matter whether one does it in one interview or five thousand. It is the end result which is important.

I hope that the discussion above will encourage patients to consult psychiatrists capable of treating them, and when they undergo treatment, to perservere until they feel normal. I hope also that it will make some psychiatrists feel that the homosexual is well worth treating. I do not think that there are any medals to be won or a great deal of money to be made in such work; but the psychiatrist may get a few grateful letters which tell how he has changed an unhappy life into a normal one and so feel adequately rewarded.

AHRENFELDT, R. H. "Homosexuality and Sexual Trauma," *British Medical Journal*, November 15, 1947.

ALLEN, C. "Adrenal Dysfunction and its Relation to sexuality," in Broster's *The Adrenal Cortex and Intersexuality*. London: Chapman and Hall, 1938.

———. "Homosexuality," in *British Encyclopedia of Medical Practice*. London, 1955.

———. *The Sexual Perversions and Abnormalities*. London: Oxford University Press, 1949.

———. "The Treatment of Homosexuality," *Medical Press* (London), CCXXXV, 441–450.

BAILEY, D. S. *Homosexuality and the Western Christian Tradition*. New York: Longmans, Green & Co., 1955.

BAUER, J. *Journal of Criminal Psychopathology*, 2.188–197 (October, 1940).

BOLITHO *Murder for Profit*. London: Dennis Dobson, 1953.

BRAMWELL, M. *Hypnotism*. London: Cassell & Co., 1909.

CAPRIO, F. S. *Female Homosexuality*. New York: The Citadel Press, 1954.

CONNOR, W. "Some Notes on Suicide," *British Journal of Medical Psychology*, 21. Part 3. 222–228 (1948).

CORY, D. *The Homosexual in America*. New York: Greenberg.

DARKE, R. "Heredity as an Etiological Factor," *Journal of*

Nervous and Mental Diseases (London), 107. 251–268 (1948).

DAVIS, K. *Factors in the Sex Life of 2200 Women.* New York, 1929.

DOSHAY, L. J. *The Boy Sex Offender and His Later Career.* New York, 1946.

EAST, N. *Society and the Criminal.* London: H. M. Stationary Office, 1949.

ELLIS, H. *Studies in the Psychology of Sex.* New York, 1936.

FORD, C. S., and BEACH, F. A. *Patterns of Sexual Behaviour.* London: Eyre and Spottiswoode, 1952.

GARDINER, A. H. (translator). *The Chester Beatty Papyri.* London: Oxford University Press, 1931.

HAILSHAM, Q. C. "Homosexuality and Society," in *They Stand Apart.* London: Heinemann, 1955.

HAMILTON, G. V. *A Research in Marriage.* New York: A. C. Boni, 1929.

———. *Journal of Animal Behaviour,* IV, 295–318 (1941).

HAMMELMANN, H. A. "Homosexuality and the Law in Other Countries." *They Stand Apart,* ed. T. Rees and H. V. Ustill. London: Heinemann, 1955.

HARRISON, T. *A Savage Civilisation.* London: Gollancz, 1937.

HENRY, G. W. *Sex Variants.* London: Cassell & Co., 1950.

HIRSCHFELD, M. *Die Homosexualität des Mannes und des Weibes.* Berlin, 1920.

JENKINS, M. *Genetic Psychological Monographs,* No. 3.457–571 (1928).

KALLMAN, F. J. *Journal of Nervous and Mental Diseases,* 115, 283–298 (1952).

KINSEY, A. C. *Journal of Clinical Endocrinology*, 1, 424–428 (1941).

———. with Pomeroy, W. B., and Gebherd, P. H. *Sexual Behavior in the Human Female*. Philadelphia: W. B. Saunders & Co.

———. *Sexual Behaviour in the Human Male*. Philadelphia: W. B. Saunders & Co.

LANGE, J. *Crime as Destiny*. London, 1930.

LONDON, L. S. *Libido and Delusion*. Washington: Mental Therapy Publications, 1945.

MACALPINE, I., and HUNTER, R. *Daniel Paul Schreiber: Memoirs of My Nervous Illness*. London: Hollen St. Press, 1956.

MYERSON, A., and NEUSTADT, R. *Clinic*, I, 942–957 (December, 1942).

PRITCHARD, J. B. *Ancient Near Eastern Texts Relating to the Old Testament*. Princeton University Press.

STANLEY-JONES, D. "Sexual Inversion and the English Law," *The Medical Press and Circular* No. 5588 (June 12, 1946).

SULLIVAN, H. S. *The Psychiatric Interview*. London: Tavistock, 1955.

SWYER, G. I. M. *The Practitioner*, 172, 374 (1954).

WEST, D. *Homosexuality*. London: Duckworth, 1955.

YERKES, D. M., and YERKES, R. M. *The Great Apes*. New Haven: Yale University Press, 1929.

ZUCKERMAN, S. *The Social Life of Monkeys and Apes*. London: Kegan Paul, 1932.

THE FOUNDATIONS OF HOMOSEXUALITY

by Charles Berg, M.D.

It is important to understand homosexuality, not only for its own sake as a psycho-social symptom, but also on account of its relationship to the various degrees of impairment of heterosexual potency so frequently encountered in almost all psychoneuroses. Furthermore, current popular interest in the subject has drawn attention to a need for whatever enlightenment psychology has to offer. The outpourings in newspapers and periodicals and the innumerable published letters, evidently emanating from people who are quite unaware of the mass of data and knowledge which science has accumulated and annotated, make one think that even a little light is better than none where all is darkness. Most of these writers do not attempt to disguise the fact that their opinions, often dogmatic, are emotionally determined—and what is more are not in any way influenced by anything other than emotion. They even boast as much! In short, our newspapers are inundated with what must be regarded as purely "*symptomatic*" opinions.

It seems unlikely that if the debate were upon a natural science, such as nuclear physics, people would be so eager to display their ignorance and to assume that their opinion or bias was other than subjective.

It has been said that few if any of us are capable of looking at sexual matters truly objectively. This is attributed to the power of the Oedipus complex in each of us. I am inclined to wonder whether *any* of us can look upon *any* matter truly objectively! When one reads some of the views expressed on most subjects, and learns of some laws and legal attitudes, ancient and modern, one may well wonder. The student is often confused at the great variety of the more or less conflicting views expressed about homosexuality, even by the greatest authorities who have written on the subject.

Nevertheless, there is a difference between even incomplete knowledge with scientific hypotheses based upon it and total ignorance with emotionally determined bias. One reason for the diversity of views may be that homosexuality is not a disease, nor even a clinical entity. It is nothing more than a particular *form of expression*, of a psychic state which is common to all living creatures. Psychic states or emotional states, impulses and longings tend, sooner or later in the course of development, to make use of some real object to assist them to achieve gratification. They tend to express themselves in what is called *object-relationship*.

For instance, the psychic state of hunger expresses itself by sucking or eating an *object*. The state of sexual "hunger," at first, expresses itself autoerotically, that is to say *without* object-relationship. Psychoanalysis has shown that every instinctual drive, every feeling or sensation, every emotional experience, gives rise to a movement in the psyche which can best be described as *unconscious phantasy*. It is a sort of dream-world, instigated principally by the sensations of physiological processes, in which the organism lives before (and after) it has very much contact with the world outside itself. Sexual feeling, (like all other sensations with their accompanying unconscious phantasies), is principally autoerotic, especially early in development; but sooner or later it tends to choose some external object, usually a person, or a part of a person, in connection with which to obtain gratification.

The *fundamental* condition is that of the sexual urge itself, emanating from the sexual instinct. A *secondary* development of this is choosing an *object* to utilise for relief of sexual tension. A further secondary development is the nature, type or sex of the *object* which seems most appropriate or convenient for this purpose.

Throughout the animal kingdom it is natural that if you cannot get one sort of food to eat, you eat or try to eat whatever sort you can get, and the evidence and data in the animal kingdom show that the same rule applies more or less to the sexual appetite also. Of course, it may still be asked why, when females are available, should a male choose another male— or indeed, as all psychiatrists have seen happen, *a lock of hair, a piece of underclothing, or even a mackintosh?* The answer to this question is generally to be found in the developmental history of the individual, if not in the phylogenetic history of the species. In short, the nature of the *object* chosen for gratification of an instinct can be a minor aberration, inherited or acquired, operating upon a psychic state common to all. Why we make such a fuss about it (I mean when it does not infringe upon any individual's liberty) is to be found in the precarious balance of forces in our own repressed unconscious— but that is another story to my mind even more interesting than the subject called homosexuality.

Having read all the literature I could find on the subject, and having spent most of my life listening to my analysands (not all of them homosexual by any means), I would like to say that I could tell the reader in a few words the nature, cause and cure of homosexuality. It would then be superfluous for him to read any other book on the subject. I am sorry that I cannot do this. We all seem to be as far from being able to do this as we are from expounding the nature, cause and cure of heterosexuality or of love—or indeed of life and the universe itself with all its manifold phenomena. Indeed, the latter task may seem to be as near to, or as far from solution as the former.

Homosexuality is a subject about which, in spite of the enormous abundance of data, there are a great many divergent views, especially of its cause and cure, and this is true even among psychiatrists. The best we can do about this subject, as about all the phenomena of nature, is to study it, sift the facts from the fancies, and go on doing this until understanding shall be thrust upon us, or so we hope.

Fifty years ago, Freud (1905) summed up the etiology of homosexuality as follows:

> The nature of inversion is explained neither by the hypothesis that it is innate nor by the alternative hypothesis that it is acquired. In the former case we must ask in what respect it is innate, unless we are to accept the crude explanation that everyone is born with his sexual instinct attached to a particular sexual object. In the latter case it may be questioned whether the various accidental influences would be sufficient to explain the acquisition of inversion without the co-operation of something in the subject himself. The existence of this last factor is not to be denied.

In this summary Freud has subsumed, on his own confession, the writings of all previous authorities including those of Kraft-Ebing, Moebus, Havelock Ellis and Magnus Hirschfeld. In the same work Freud goes on to say:

> It has been brought to our notice that we have been in the habit of regarding the connection between the sexual instinct and the sexual object as more intimate than it in fact is. Ex-

perience of the cases that are considered abnormal has shown us that in them the sexual instinct and the sexual object are merely soldered together—a fact which we have been in danger of overlooking in consequence of the uniformity of the normal picture where the object appears to form part and parcel of the instinct. We are thus warned to loosen the bond that exists in our thoughts between instinct and object. It seems probable that the sexual instinct is in the first instance independent of its object; nor is its origin likely to be due to its object's attractions'.

We may well ask what progress in our knowledge has been made in this half century, despite increase in the data available. These data appear to be quite inexhaustible and of every variety. And yet C. H. Rolph (1955) can write (in the B.S.B. Council's book on female prostitution):

> I will surely show . . . that all the punitive legislation in the world could make no real impression on this problem [female prostitution]. It is a problem in essence of parent-and-child, its solution lies in happy homes and the manifold securities that are to be found in them. *The same is almost certainly true of that other moral outcast, the male homosexual, whose position before the law is, as I write, once more the focus of public controversy. But of that problem,* and even of what is called male prostitution, *still less is known.* The British Social Biology Council are now organising, as a logical sequel to this report, a similar research into male prostitution in London, a first step towards a fuller examination of the entire social problem of homosexuality. [My italics.]

But the data of research, if we are to avoid a misleading, narrow, parochial point of view should, like the data of anatomy, physiology, psychology and sociology, extend beyond sociology, beyond a study limited to homo sapiens. To

obtain an adequate perspective the field of research should begin, if not with chemistry and physics, at least biologically,
with the lower animals.

We have space to consider only a few excerpts from this
wide field: Jenkins (1928) found that if rats were segregated
sexually and no possible contact with the other sex allowed,
after some time homosexual behaviour would commence. This
grew in proportion to the length of segregation. If later he introduced animals of the opposite sex these conditioned homosexuals showed little heterosexual interest. He found that the
number of those which regained their heterosexuality was
proportionately dependent upon the length of time they had
been segregated. The longer the segregation, the greater the
number of rats which showed diminished sexuality on mixing
with the other sex.

Dr. Allen (1940) says: "So strong is the instinct to copulate that an animal, and presumably a man, will attempt to perform sexual congress with unsuitable partners if no suitable
ones are available." Margaret Mead (1949) asks: "When human beings—or rats—are conditioned by social circumstances
to respond sexually to members of their own sex as adults and
in preference to members of the opposite sex, is this conditioning playing on a real bisexual base in the personality, which
varies greatly in its structure as between one member of a
group and another?"

It may be added that so far as human beings are concerned,
homosexual "conditioning," if of any importance, would seem
to depend for its effectiveness on its being introduced before
the child or infant had developed a heterosexual tendency or
pattern. Yet I have known many cases where boys were

seduced, even by adult males, and, though seemingly behaving homosexually, were at the most merely pseudo-homosexuals; they showed no homosexual tendencies after puberty. In normal persons heterosexual patterns are established, at least in the unconscious mind, very long before puberty, probably in babyhood, though not necessarily to the defensive exclusion of homosexual behaviour.

On the other hand, I have recently seen a young married man with a family of several children who wept to me over his compulsive addiction to lavatory meetings with unknown male seducers. He says it first happened to him unexpectedly when he was sixteen years of age and apparently exceptionally innocent. Though he fled in terror on that occasion, he has returned to the same spot and similar spots periodically in the hope, frequently realised, that the opportunity might again present itself—and this is in spite of his evident terror of discovery. This would seem like an instance of clear-cut conditioning, but I am convinced that a deeper investigation will show other elements in his psychopathology, possibly even a fundamental homosexual trend and a current pseudo-heterosexuality. This last phenomenon is more common than is generally appreciated.

It is particularly interesting that this patient originally consulted me on account of ideas of reference (paranoid or delusional ideas) that persons in his office were looking at him suspiciously. This sort of thing is common enough in psychiatric experience and supports Freud's original view that paranoia (from which I believe we all tend to suffer in a mild way) is psychopathologically founded upon repressed, unconscious homosexuality.

I feel that the converse mechanism suggested by Mayer-Gross (1954) when he says: "Freud has commented on the frequency of a homosexual component in paranoid psychoses; it seems possible that for this finding social rather than constitutional or infantile psychodynamic factors are responsible," is mistaken and is putting the cart before the horse. At the most such factors, fear of social disgrace and blackmail, can act only secondarily, or as adjuvants, on the psychopathological basis of *repressed* elements in the homosexual conflict. Further, when Mayer-Gross goes on to hint that "understanding, tolerance and sympathetic advice" can have any real influence on the course of homosexual behaviour, I feel that he is too optimistic. Homosexuality and paranoia are often comparably obstinate therapeutically to a degree which may in itself suggest a relationship in psychopathology.

Another young man at a hospital out-patient department told me that for many years he had been sleeping with his girl friend because he had been encouraged to do so by a doctor whom he consulted. He then came out with the illuminating statement that that doctor could "not have had a clue" of what he was talking about nor the slightest understanding of him, the patient. His grounds for this criticism of the doctor were expressed as follows: "This sort of sex does not help me in the slightest. I am in just as awful a condition inside, if not worse. What I am thinking about and longing for all the time is sex *with a man*, and that is the only experience which brings me any satisfaction, and makes me feel at peace again." I may mention that this patient is in appearance a healthy, normal young specimen of manhood, in spite of his acute anxiety symptoms and his somewhat overneat grooming.

The late Dr. Hirschfeld, probably the most experienced of all sexologists, said (1938) that the diagnosis of genuine homosexuality must depend not only upon "involuntary mental and spiritual fixation on one's own sex, striving for an outlet in sexual activity, but also upon the *absence of normal heterosexual affinity*." (His third criterion, namely that of "intersexual constitution," does not seem to be applicable in all cases).

In the same way as the physical and physiological development of man can best be illuminated by such researches as those of Darwin in biology, so the fundamental nature or source of his psychological peculiarities is commonly best illuminated by study of animal and infant behaviour, particularly by a study of the higher mammals, such as monkeys. One has the advantage here of observing Nature at work without the inhibiting and concealing effects of superimposed human culture. There have been many researchers in this field. Kinsey (1953) says:

> The impression that infra-human mammals more or less confine themselves to heterosexual activities is a distortion of the fact which appears to have originated in a man-made philosophy . . . in actuality sexual contacts between individuals of the same sex are known to occur in practically every species of mammal which has been extensively studied. In many species homosexual contacts may occur with considerable frequency though never as frequently as heterosexual contacts.
>
> Homosexual contacts in infra-human species of mammals occur among both females and males. Homosexual contacts between females have been observed in such widely separated species as rats, mice, hamsters, guinea pigs, rabbits, porcupines, martens, cattle, antelope, goats, horses, pigs, lions, sheep, monkeys and chimpanzees.

Apparently orgasm in the female animals is uncertain, but "sexual contacts between males of the lower mammalian species do proceed to the point of orgasm, at least for the male that mounts another male."

(An English farmer of sixty years standing told me that it was quite common to see cows mounting other cows, and he vouchsafed the information that the cow doing the mounting was by that act alone demonstrating that she was particularly ready for the bull. But what he considered still more curious was that the cow being mounted also showed readiness in this direction, more so than the cattle which did not partake in this.)

Kinsey concludes:

> The mammalian record thus confirms our statement that any animal which is not too strongly conditioned by some special sort of experience is capable of responding to any adequate stimulus. This is what we find in the more uninhibited segments of our own human species, and this is what we find among young children who are not too rigorously restrained in their early sex play. Exclusive preferences and patterns of behaviour, heterosexual or homosexual, come only with experience, or as a result of social pressures which tend to force an individual into an exclusive pattern of one or the other sort . . . *It is more difficult to explain why each and every individual is not involved in every type of sexual activity.* (My italics)

I think the biologist would say that the reason here is largely to do with internal secretions, endocrines and odours. On the other hand attempts to influence homosexuality by hormones has resulted in increase of erotic interest and capacity, *but without any change whatsoever in object-choice.*

The psychoanalyst would say that the choice of object is largely determined by a succession of early events, beginning at the breast, until the pattern is established. If we do not confine our attention to one individual life, I am convinced that in spite of modern biological theories we may extend this conditioning phylogenetically to the beginning of life, introducing, if we like, the Darwinian principle of natural and of sexual selection to ensure the maintenance of heterosexuality as the surviving pattern of behaviour.

Anthropological data are even more abundant than those provided by the biologists and monkey-observers, in spite of Havelock Ellis's interesting complaint (1901) that

> the travellers and others on whose records we are dependent have been so shy of touching these subjects, and so ignorant of the main points for investigation, that it is very difficult to discover sexual inversion in the proper sense in any lower race. Travellers have spoken vaguely of crimes against nature without defining the precise relationship involved nor inquiring how far any congenital impulse could be distinguished.

Malinowski (1929), according to Reich's (1942) "summary," was not so "shy and ignorant." He found that:

> Children in the Trobriand islands know . . . no sexual secrecy. Their sex life is allowed to develop naturally, freely and unhampered *through every stage of life, with full satisfaction.* The children engage freely in the sexual activities which correspond to their age . . . the Trobrianders knew . . . no sexual perversions, no functional psychoses, no psychoneuroses, no sex murder: They have no word for theft; homosexuality and masturbation, to them, mean nothing but an unnatural and imperfect means of sexual gratification . . . The socially accepted form of sexual life is spontaneous monogamy

without compulsion, a relationship which can be dissolved without difficulties; thus, there is no promiscuity.

Reich goes on to say:

> At the time when Malinowski made his studies of the Trobriand islanders, there was living a few miles away, on the Amphlett Islands, a tribe with patriarchal authoritarian family organisation. The people inhabiting these islands were already showing all the traits of the European neurotic, such as distrust, anxiety, neuroses, perversion, suicide, etc.

Reich concludes:

> The determining factor of the mental health of a population is the condition of its natural love life.

There is not space in this study to give adequate consideration to the data accumulated since Ellis's complaint, and extending beyond his survey, which covers material from ancient Egypt, Carthage, the introduction into Greece of *paederastia* by the Dorian warriors, Persia, Constantinople, China, India, Afghanistan, American Indians from the Eskimos of Alaska to Brazil and farther south, various parts of Africa, the Papuans of New Guinea, Russia, Rome, Germany and France. Every degree of homosexuality seems to have prevailed in different places and at different times, accompanied by every degree of reaction-formation, varying from "fashion" in ancient Greece, and official promotion, sanction or toleration, to the direst penalties, including the death sentence. Havelock Ellis points out that as late as the eighteenth century in London, when homosexual practices were "more prevalent . . . than today," "the punishment for sodomy, when completely effected, was death, and it was frequently inflicted."

The modern equivalent of these reactive expressions is comparably savage. The Offences Against the Person Act, 1861, regarding what it calls "the abominable crime of buggery," says, the culprit is ". . . *to be kept in penal servitude for life or for any term not less than ten years*," making it clear that the State claims monopoly of the act. Mayer-Gross (1954) says: "In Switzerland, Scandinavia and Germany some of these offenders have been treated by castration, when freely submitted to." (One may wonder how "free" was the submission). A disadvantage in such cases is that the psychiatrist may subsequently have to deal with an intractable depression.

It is noteworthy, if only as a corrective to biased conclusions, that some of the most notable persons in history were, according to Havelock Ellis "All charged, on more or less solid evidence, with homosexual practices." His list includes such names as Julius Caesar, alleged to have been "the husband of all women and the wife of all men," Augustus, Tiberius, Caligula, Claudius, Nero, Hadrian, "many of them men of great ability, and, from a Roman standpoint, great moral worth."

It would be interesting if we could discover whether, in accordance with Freudian psychopathology, all these could be shown to have had an exaggerated emotional attachment to their mothers, deriving from earliest Oedipus-incestuous infancy. Mayer-Gross says: "What we have learnt about the life history of famous men such as André Gide and Marcel Proust, who were self-confessed homosexuals, certainly suggests that an intense emotional attachment to the mother may play a part in some cases."

Mayer-Gross goes on to say: "As a matter of clinical experience it is remarkable how often homosexuals are of more than average intelligence." Indeed, if one studies the illustrious names right up to almost modern times, one may feel that there is some excuse for the inverts' ridiculous claim of a monopoly of culture and genius. Leonardo da Vinci, perhaps the greatest artist of all time, was certainly imprisoned in his youth on account of it. Freud (1916) points out that Leonardo was "disgusted" with everything heterosexual and concludes that his temperament was marked by "ideal homosexuality"—"it may be thought by far more probable that the affectionate relationships of Leonardo to the young men did not result in sexual activity."

Ellis writes: "Michelangelo, one of the very chief artists of the Renaissance period, we cannot now doubt, was sexually inverted." The list goes on to include such august names as Virgil, Sophocles, Alexander the Great, Frederick the Great, Wagner; and in England, William Rufus, Edward II, James I, and "perhaps William III." Literary figures are not spared: Marlowe and Francis Bacon are strongly suspected, and even Shakespeare "narrowly escapes." And so on, to include Edward Fitzgerald and Walt Whitman, until we reach "the most famous homosexual trial of recent times in England," that of Oscar Wilde. Concerning this trial, Ellis says with regard to *psychopathology:*

> Although this development (Oscar Wilde's homosexual behaviour) occurred comparatively late in life, we must hesitate to describe Wilde's homosexuality as acquired. If we consider his constitution and his history, it is not difficult to suppose that homosexual germs were present in latent form from the first, and it may quite well be that Wilde's inversion was of that kind which is now described as retarded, though still congenital.

With regard to *reaction*, Ellis says: "There arose a general howl of execration, joined in even by the judge." The same sort of thing can be witnessed in magistrates' courts today.

All this may be regarded as collateral evidence in favour of Kinsey's (1948) contention that "perhaps the *major portion* of the male population has at least some homosexual experience between adolescence and old age." Kinsey goes on to say: "In addition, some *sixty per cent* of pre-adolescent boys engage in homosexual activities and there is an additional group of adult males who avoid overt contacts but are quite aware of their potentialities for reacting to other males." Kinsey, basing his conclusions upon the greatest statistical evidence yet achieved in this field, continues: "There is only about half of the male population whose sexual behaviour is exclusively heterosexual." I consider his view that "one must learn to recognise every combination of heterosexuality and homosexuality in the histories of various individuals" as somewhat misleading, not of mere *acts*, for there he has the data, nor of the unconscious mind, which certainly contains everything, but misleading as a manifestation of *true* sexuality, that is to say of sexual behaviour which brings the fullest gratification. This is because I consider that heterosexual *activities* are *pseudo*-heterosexuality in many genuine homosexuals, and for that matter homosexuality also can be *pseudo-*, particularly in boys and young people. I refer to sexual activity which is not genuinely or fully in line with the psycho-sexual phantasy and impulse, and which therefore does not achieve adequate psycho-sexual satisfaction. It is nevertheless commonly practised, especially among women—notably in marriage and notoriously in prostitution. A case illustrating this discrepancy be-

tween sexual phantasy and sexual practice in a married man is
described below.

With regard to theory and the vexed question as to
whether homosexuality is constitutional or acquired, there is
every gradation of conflicting opinion from antiquity to the
present day. Ellis reminds us: "Aristotle also, in his fragment
on physical love, though treating the whole matter with indulgence, seems to have distinguished abnormal congenital
homosexuality from acquired homosexual vice." It seems that
the best course is to keep on accumulating data, and proceeding to deeper investigation of the mind, before this problem
can be satisfactorily unravelled.

It is possible that Freud's theory, already quoted above,
which attributes homosexuality to early experiences *combined
with* congenital factors, such as bisexuality in the unconscious
and personal sexual make-up, will become the most favoured.
In the meantime, there are many data to reinforce the various
controversial leanings regarding causation.

It is commonly held, as Krich (1954) points out, that "the
chief arguments *against* the psychogenic explanation of homosexuality centre around the undeniable fact that some persons
subjected to a particular set of pressures become homosexuals,
while others *in the same circumstances* do not." In my own
professional experience I have often been, as it were, startled
into the environmentalists' point of view by clinical evidence
of some homosexual event thrust upon a person, especially
at puberty or adolescence, which he subsequently appears to
be compulsively re-seeking in surprisingly detailed exactitude.
I have already referred to this in the case of the young married
man who waited for a repetition of the identical event which

he experienced in a lavatory at the age of sixteen. Magistrates and judges and perhaps the public at large appear to be "sold" on this etiological idea, but the facts of a wider experience certainly fail to support it. I have *also* heard much clinical detail of patients who were homosexually seduced in a variety of circumstances, particularly at school, and who subsequently emerged as heterosexual and as normal as anyone. So the problem of causation is not solved by such clinical instances.

I am convinced that an important determinant in the causation of homosexuality is, at least in many cases, similar to that of fetishism. Here it would seem that the sexual object, or rather the object that stimulates sexuality, must have a purely symbolical significance, and that such symbolic significance must have been acquired at an extremely early age, usually during the period of infantial amnesia.

How else, for instance, can one account for such an incident as the following, told me by a mackintosh fetishist? At the age of nineteen he was taken by his rather "fast" young girl friend into her bedroom, presumably for some love-making; but in spite of her passes he was and remained psychologically quite unaware of any desire for the girl. Instead, he was all eyes for her mackintosh which hung on the doorpeg! This he stared at with rapt attention; he clearly remembers his mounting sexual excitement and tumescence. He was not conscious of any tendency to connect this excitement with the girl herself.

It is difficult to think of such a peculiar proclivity as being inherited. Can one possibly assume an *inherited* predilection for mackintoshes as one's sexual object? They are obviously in such cases a *symbol* for something sexually exciting that has itself been completely repressed from consciousness. Freud says "The true explanation (of fetishism) is that behind the first recollection of the fetish's appearance there lies a submerged and forgotten phase of sexual development. The fetish, like a 'screen-memory,' represents this phase and is thus a remnant and precipitate of it. The fact that this early infantile phase turns in the direction of fetishism, as well as the choice of the fetish itself, are constitutionally determined." I may mention that the mackintosh fetishist above referred to improved to the degree of marrying, having children and enjoying marital sexual experience. But I am still convinced that some of the potentialities for heterosexual enjoyment remain unconscious in him. Mackintoshes still augment his sexual pleasure.

May not the difficulty in recognising some of the acquired causes of homosexuality be laid at the door of some such mechanisms as those responsible for fetishism. In other words, there appears to me to be evidence that, at least in some cases, perhaps in many if not in all, the "object" of the sexual excitement, be it man or mackintosh, is stimulating an unconscious mechanism in the mind similar to that responsible for fetishism. When we find a man using another man as though he were a female may he not be making a similar "mistake" to that made by our mackintosh fetishist; and similarly when a feminine woman chooses as her lover a person of her own sex? The question may be more difficult to answer in the case of the passive male homosexual and the active, or masculine female homosexual. It seems to me possible that these latter are more constitutionally determined, whereas the aforementioned may be fetishistically determined. Nevertheless, as many writers have pointed out, in homosexuals the role is usually interchangeable.

However, I should admit that in my opinion the strongest arguments against the psychogenic explanation of homosexuality are not in accordance with the views above referred to by Krich. It would seem to me that the strongest proof of hereditary factors in homosexuality, as in many other abnormalities, could be provided by a study of uniovular twins, or to use the American term, "monozygotic pairs." In a study published in 1952 of a consecutive series of eighty-five plainly homosexual twin index cases, Dr. Franz J. Kallman found that "in every case of forty homosexuals who had a monozygotic twin, the twin, after adolescence, was found to have exactly the same overt homosexual practice and with the same quantitative reading of homosexual behaviour." In other words, like all uniovular twins, they were as like as two peas in the nature and quantity of their homosexual practices. The author claims that all these pairs, forty in number, denied any mutual sexual relationship and claimed to have developed the homosexual pattern independently of each other and far apart from each other. What is more, he says that the individuals of each pair had so marked a sexual taboo between them that each disclaimed knowledge of any intimate details of his co-twin's sex life.

The remaining forty-five twin pairs of the eighty-five pairs investigated were dizygotic, or binovular, twins and the co-twin of each of these homosexual subjects did not generally show any homosexual leanings. There were homosexuals among them, but "only slightly in excess of Kinsey's rating for the total male population." It certainly would seem that this investigation diminishes the plausibility of environmental causes, such as parental incompetence, for in both these groups, the forty pairs and the forty-five pairs, the childhood of each of each pair was spent in a similar environment to that of his twin, parentally and otherwise. Only the uniovular twins developed identical patterns as regards their overt homosexual practice and the quantity of it. Corroborating these findings, Mayer-Gross tells us that: "Sanders (1934) has reported seven uniovular pairs with one member homosexual; in six of these the other twin was homosexual also. Similar observations have been made by Lange, Hirschfeld, Spiro, etc."

In addition to mental and behaviouristic deviations we are reminded by Mayer-Gross that "A certain proportion of male homosexuals . . . show a deficient growth of hair on face and body, tend to have high voices, to show a more feminine type of distribution of body fat. According to Henry, measurements of the bony pelvis also tend to deviate similarly from the norm in homosexuals of either sex." Of course, this is true only of "a certain proportion" of homosexuals. A suggestion has been made by Myerson and Neustadt (1942) that "androgen concentration [in the urine] determines the vigour of sex drive, the absolute or proportionate amount of oestrogens its direction." The authors of *Clinical Psychiatry* (1954) think that "it would be surprising if adequate further research did not lay a sure basis in a physical and most probably endocrine deviation."

Nevertheless, I am of the opinion that these considerations do not put an end to the importance of psychological factors in this problem any more than Mendelian laws and other discoveries regarding hereditary and congenital factors put an end to the importance of psychological and environmental factors in the finer details of human behaviour and beliefs. For instance, in the choice of love-object or sex-object it has been abundantly demonstrated that, from rats to mankind, in the absence of the opposite sex, one's own sex is likely to be utilised and a homosexual conditioning more or less established, if only temporarily. There is no doubt that whatever we inherit—and it may well be the foundation of everything that is us—including all our instinctual tendencies, at least the finer details of our reactions, thoughts and attitudes are profoundly influenced by environment, and particularly, as psychoanalysis has discovered, by our earliest experiences in the first few days, weeks, months and years of our individual life. Agreed that if two people are different to start with, they will react differently to similar environmental experiences. Indeed, one of a pair may collect within his psyche certain of these experiences, excluding others; and the other may collect other experiences and *block* many of those which impressed his opposite number. This is where the uniovular twin investigation comes in, because here each individual was from the identical egg and therefore, unlike a binovular twin, reacted identically in babyhood to presumably identical stimulation. The advocates of the congenital theory tell us that what we start with biologically pre-disposes us to certain reactive patterns; but there is no doubt that individual experience has some effect or influence upon the modification of inherited patterns, the formation of new reactive patterns, and upon the continuation or otherwise of patterns acquired after birth.

The congenitalists have a mass of evidence in favour of their contentions, and we look for still more evidence and enlightenment from them. Psychology and psychoanalysis should not, and do not, deny congenital and physical factors, somatic and instinctual. Indeed, they insist that instinct (by definition inherited) is the basis of all our behaviour. Psychology and psychoanalysis investigate mental mechanisms, the mind's reaction to instinctual gratifications and frustrations, and the production and development of the mental process of unconscious phantasy on these bases. Psychoanalysis has shown that these unconscious phantasies activate or influence our behaviour and beliefs. Finer details such as fetishism, for instance the mackintosh fetishism above referred to, must have their source in acquired reactive patterns rather than in inheritance. I have hinted also that such "minor" aberrations as other object-choice, including the homosexual, may well belong to the finesse of acquired reactive patterns with their utilisation of the mechanism of symbolism, than to anything more in the congenital department than some hereditary predisposition.

There is no doubt in my mind that fetishistic mechanisms play a part in all sexual object-choice, whether heterosexual or homosexual. Ferenczi (1916) points out that the buttocks can unconsciously symbolise the woman's breasts. This would be applicable for the buttocks of either sex. In the same paper, he mentions also that sadistic and anal erotic impulses can be replaced by reaction formations resulting in "sublimated or over-refined boys' love with an anxious shunning of all indecent contacts." In other words, what enters consciousness is determined by a balance of conflicting forces, impulses and repressing mechanisms from the unconscious. These are very fine adjustments of a mixture of acquired and inherited forces, the results of which, though hanging on a thread, as it were, may appear to be so very different to the observer. As Dr. Kallmann (1952) says: "The most plausible explanation for this [homosexual] finding is that the axis around which the organisation of personality and sex function takes place is *so easily dislocated* that attainment of a maturational balance may be disarranged at different developmental stages and by a *variety of disturbing mechanisms*." (My italics.) We cannot therefore afford to exclude a study of psychological considerations even if we do accept the congenitalists' point of view. Heredity directly affects mainly trends or tendencies and the balance of instincts. Such considerations help us to understand the different, and, at first sight apparently antithetical, points of view.

Dr. Clara Thompson (1949) emphasises that "homosexuality is not a clinical entity but a symptom with different meanings in different personality set-ups." Like any human action, homosexuality—like heterosexuality—*means* something different in each individual . . . and in the same individual at different times and in different contexts. A handshake, or the touch of another person's hand, or having one's own hand touched by another person, may have a thousand different meanings and carry with it a thousand different subjective experiences. Apparently homosexual acts of the same, or different, variety can have many different meanings. Therefore, it is often erroneous to extract a common denominator even for acts which appear to be identical. Here, for instance, is a clinical excerpt which may cause the clinician to make different guesses at different stages of enlightenment:

I was once consulted by a deformed male midget, aged forty and about the size of a boy of eight. He came to me because he was very distressed, depressed and suicidal. The story that unfolded was this. For a decade and a half he had been living with a married couple who were childless. They had, as it were, "adopted" him; for, though intellectually adult, he was emotionally very immature. Now this dwarf was in the habit of sitting in the lap of his adopted father, who presumably was a heterosexual man. At this stage of the story, the psychological meaning was evidently that the dwarf was experiencing the feelings of a little boy being loved by Daddy. Was there anything homosexual in this? Every little boy, and that was the degree of immaturity the dwarf possessed, likes to sit on Daddy's lap. However, in due course, the patient confessed to me that this experience of sitting in his foster-father's lap was usually, though not always, accompanied by his having some degree of erection. Still later he confessed that his erotic feeling was accompanied by a desire to fondle "father's" penis. Eventually it came about that desire was implemented by action. For very many years this had been the only alloerotic life which this dwarf had found available. When finally it had been ended by the wife's intervention, my patient had a nervous breakdown with all the sensations of the most devastating bereavement—mourning, melancholia, and death wishes. Analytical transference appeared to rescue him only just in time. If he had needed the sexual outlet to reduce tension and anxiety, it seemed that the re-living of childhood with a good-parent-figure was even more important for his health and happiness. Not every infant is treated to *overt* incestuous relationships (!), but analysis reveals that a greater or lesser degree of this is experienced as an *unconscious* accompaniment of normal contact with parents and parent surrogates, together with defensive reactions against it. Unconscious phantasy supplies that which reality frustrates and denies.

In passing from the theory of congenital to that of environmental causes of homosexuality, we should perhaps pause for a moment, but only for a moment, at that term "bi-sexual" which has evidently been invented in the hope of clarifying the problem. I think it leads to more confusion and misconception than to clarification. Admittedly, in the *unconscious* mind there is room for every contradiction to live side by side, and room for every variety or level of sexuality and every variety of object-choice. Jung says normal men cover the feminine component of their psyche ("anima") with a masculine mask and normal women cover their masculine component ("animus") with a feminine mask. Ernest Jones (1935) seems to have a lingering doubt about the matter. Although he says, "the assumption of inborn bisexuality seems to me a very probable one, in favour of which many biological facts can be quoted," he adds later, "I do not think we should take it absolutely for granted." Stekel (1922) appears to solve the problem to his satisfaction when he says: "There is no inborn homosexuality and no inborn heterosexuality. There is only *bisexuality*. Monosexuality already involves a predisposition to neurosis and in many cases stands for the neurosis proper." I think he is dead right for the unconscious mind, and probably in his concluding remark too.

The following case vividly illustrates this sort of thing. A married man consulted me on account of a variety of acute and chronic anxiety symptoms accompanied by despondency, depression, lack of concentration, lassitude, incapacity for work and the familiar polysymptomatology. He told me that his wife had just returned from the nursing home where she had had their baby. He felt he could not bear her presence in his house. Questioning elicited the fact that he had been psychosexually impotent until she, out of her love for him, had painstakingly taught him to have coitus. The degree of "proficiency" he had acquired certainly left much to be desired. In fact, his so-called coitus amounted to a succession of effortful manual endeavours with an unwilling, detumescing orgasm. The result was usually total failure leaving him exhausted and irritable. I asked him what was his *natural* sexual life, and he replied, "masturbation." He declared that this was without phantasy. Oh no, he certainly never had phantasies of a female, in whole or in part. This he said would have resulted in the immediate subsidence of his erection. Then he confessed that, during masturbation, he did occasionally phantasy a young man. The phantasy was that he would seek the young man's penis, make it erect and admire it. No, he had never tried this. It would be just "too exciting." He added: "I would throw myself in the river, if I thought I were a homosexual." The conclusion is inescapable that in his unconscious phantasy this homosexual, married man is terrified of the female genitals.

It is possible to say two things about the etiology of his anxiety neurosis: (1) that his libido is being frustrated and inhibited from any adequate gratifying outlet; and (2) that attempts to coerce it, in the face of his phobia, into a heterosexual channel, is increasing his nervous strain and exacerbating his neurosis. Further, one may ask whether what this case shows up in such strong relief is not (in a lesser degree and in a relatively inconspicuous way) common to all members of civilised communities—namely, a sexual outlet which does not exactly coincide with the individual's unconscious phantasy, or a more or less effortful sexual behaviour contrary to that phantasy.

Is this the sort of thing that Stekel means when he says that "monosexuality [heterosexuality *or* homosexuality] already involves a predisposition to neurosis and in many cases stands for the neurosis proper?" I think it is certainly in keeping with Reich's (1942) tenet that neurosis is always formed out of the residue of inadequately relieved libido. "Orgastic impotence

. . . provides the source of energy for all kinds of psychic and somatic symptoms." "The basis of the disturbances is a deviation from the natural modes of discharge" ("natural" for that particular individual.) "Relapse into neurosis after psychoanalytic cure may be averted to the extent to which orgastic satisfaction in the sexual act is assured." "The essence of a neurosis is the inability of the patient to obtain gratification."

If we add to this, ". . . to obtain gratification in his object-relationships in adequate co-incidence with the wishes of his unconscious phantasy," then perhaps we have the essence of the immediate factor in the above mentioned case of anxiety neurosis. I would add that *in so far as reality and unconscious phantasy do not coincide, to that degree will a corresponding quantity and quality of reactive, perverse or neurotic character traits, symptoms or behaviour be inevitable.*

According to psychoanalysis the newly-born baby begins its sexual life at the oral level, its object-choice being the breast or nipple. Subsequently, when through development, the genital level has acquired erotic primacy, the object-choice is not necessarily or totally the whole-object-personality, as well as body, of a person of the opposite sex. Even in the most normal a certain amount of libido is left by the wayside or taken up with part-objects and what I call minor degrees of fetishism, whether these relate to breasts, hair, legs, figure or clothes. Symbolism, fetishism proper and homosexuality are only extreme degrees of this. The term "bi-sexual" is misleading because, on a *conscious* level, that is to say a behaviouristic level (unlike at an unconscious level), there is a tendency for the mind to be more integrated and to reject one or other of two opposing impulses, objects or phantasies. As Bergler (1948) says, "Nobody can dance at two weddings at the same time, not even the wizard of a homosexual." Although, as he admits, it *is* possible for some homosexuals to have "erective potency in a lustless coitus," it would be misleading to call them bi-sexual on this account. I think the truth is that if one sex is associated with gratification the other sex tends to be associated with castration. The degree or intensity of this antithesis may vary from one individual to another.

Even Kinsey with his seven-point scale based upon relative frequency of "outlet" between homosexuality and heterosexuality deprecates the term "bi-sexual" as untenable. He deals similarly with the term "intersex": "In spite of the fact that Goldschmidt himself (1916) accepted the idea that the homosexual human male or female was an intersex, there is no adequate basis for reaching any such conclusion." In biology the term would mean an individual with a portion or a whole of its structure intermediate in character between the structure of the typical male and that of the typical female of the species.

Nevertheless, the fact cannot be denied that individuals do exist who both physically and mentally exhibit strikingly marked characteristics of the opposite sex. It should be remembered that such persons are not necessarily homosexual in the correct clinical or behaviouristic sense. In spite of their contrasexual characteristics they may actually have no sexual attraction towards members of their own sex. Although it may be true to say that the two sexes are on a mental plane not sharply differentiated and that on a physical plane each shows many physical characteristics of the other, and that these are subject to every degree and variation, nevertheless pronounced anomalies do exist and give some justification or excuse for Lang's (1940) *intersex* theory. Mayer-Gross appears to favour this theory of homosexuality and goes so far as to emphasise the possibility from the fact that "sex is determined, not by a gene or group of genes, but by a *balance being struck between opposing groups of genes.*" This may be very interesting and true, but it may not have as much bearing on homosexuality as would appear at first sight. This is because as the authors themselves admit: *"Physical constitution and mental attitude are not closely connected."* (My italics.) And "homosexuality" is a term that applies to a mental attitude and not to physical constitution. Indeed, it might be true to say that a "diagnosis" based on characteristics no deeper than the *unconscious* mind (even without morphology and genetics) would have to declare everybody bisexual *and* less or more of an intersex. As I have said, diagnosis has to be based on conscious and manifest trends and on behaviour. This level alone is appropriate for the clinical diagnosis of any and every condition. These terms, bisexual and intersex, though not negligible by any means, are misleading because they imply desires and behaviour that are contrary to the facts, because it seems that at conscious and manifest levels one *form* of sexuality is preferred. If this form does not absolutely exclude all others (which it often does), it tends at least to result in a marked preferential presidence of itself over all others. "Nobody can dance at two weddings at the same time, not even the wizard of a homosexual."

With reference to the above material in general, I would like to express my doubts as to whether the physical mechanisms of any process can provide us with anything more than a illusion of the solution of a problem. I have always felt this way about the biological theory of *mutations* as an "explanation" of the evolutionary process. Genes do not explain mutations;

and mutations (even with the aid of natural-selection) do not explain evolution. Admittedly the concept of "a balance being struck between opposing groups of genes" is a little more plausible. If "accidents" do happen in nature they cannot be regarded as accidental but only as an aspect of the operation of the law of cause and effect. Might this balance or imbalance of genes be just another such instance of the law of cause and effect, resulting in variants that may perform functions other than those of reproduction? A neuter sex has proved helpful to survival of the Hymenoptera. A species progresses as does a multicellular organism, by the development of devious capacities for adjustment to its enviornment apart from those of reproduction. The conception of bisexuality and intersex may be very useful in a biological study but may prove more misleading than helpful in solving the behaviouristic problem of homosexuality.

We are left then with the two etiological theories, the congenital and the acquired, the first being the province of biology and the second of psychology, the first relating to all that is inherited including hereditary predispositions, and the second concerned only with the finer adjustments of reactive patterns to individual experiences and enviornment. Neither of these can by itself provide a complete answer to the manifold problems presented by any behaviouristic phenomenon. They are thus mutually dependent rather than antagonistic. Let us now go a little more deeply into the environmental or psychological aspect of etiology.

As a condensation of the *psychoanalytical* point of view a few excerpts from Fenichel's great book, *The Psychoanalytical Theory of Neurosis* (1946), are representative:

Initially everyone is able to develop sexual feelings indiscriminately, and the search for an object is less limited by the sex of the object than is commonly supposed. . . . The fact that in a normal person the object-choice later becomes more or less limited to the opposite sex is a problem in itself. . . . Since the homosexual, like any other human being, originally has the capacity to choose objects of either sex, what limits this capacity to objects of his own sex? . . . Analysis of homosexual men regularly shows that they are afraid of female genitals. . . . The female genitals, through the connection of castration anxiety with oral anxieties, may be perceived as a castrating instrument capable of biting or tearing off the penis.

These morbid fears, arising from these unconscious phantasies, are commonly rationalised by homosexuals into such forms, for instance, as "fear of pregnancy" and "fear of venereal disease." Incidentally, Dr. T. Anwyl-Davies, the leading venereologist, tells me that venereal disease is at least as common among homosexuals as heterosexuals. Mayer-Gross says homosexuals "tend to be more promiscuous than heterosexual persons," but adds, "the romantic element in passion may be as strong or stronger."

Regarding the impression, perhaps unduly stressed by Ferenczi (1916), that homosexuals can be divided into passive homosexuals or inverts on the one hand, and *object* homoerotics, who, in the case of males, remain masculine in their behaviour, merely choosing another male as though he were a female, it is worth remembering that in the majority of homosexuals a reversal of roles is more the rule than the exception. Mayer-Gross says:

Male homosexuals are frequently classified into the active and the passive type; female homosexuals into the masculine and feminine. The active male homosexual is defined as one who in sexual relationships with another male takes the active role making his partner adopt the female position in intercourse, or to submit to, rather than to perform, sodomy, etc. The active physical role is usually accompanied by the active, seeking, courting and dominating role mentally. . . . *Mutatis mutandis* the same may be said for female homosexuals. The active male and the passive female are frequently of fairly normal psychosomatic constitution; . . . The passive male and the active female homosexual are much more likely to show contrasexual traits of physique and mind, and to be irreversibly and solely homosexually inclined.

There is, however, *no sharp distinction between activity and passivity,* as a lasting trait, . . . Furthermore the mental and physical aspects of activity or passivity may not go together. . . . reversal of roles may occur between the same partners on different occasions. Even with these reservations, however, it is broadly true that homosexuals tend to fall into one or other of these two classes and not to be unclassifiably midway between.

Fenichel says:

Terms like subject homo-erotic and object homo-erotic have only relative significance. Active homosexuality in a man may serve to repress a deeper passive homosexual longing and vice versa . . . combinations of both types of homosexuality occur. These types constitute the majority of all male homosexualities, but occasionally other types occur.

There is a very prevalent type, originally described by Freud, as "mild" homosexuals, which is characterised by extreme friendliness towards persons of one's own sex. Fenichel says: "Homosexual love of this type, which according to Freud contributes largely to that which later forms 'social feelings' is mixed with characteristics of identification." It is generally agreed that there is an element of "identification with the object" in all homosexual love.

It may seem that the psychoanalytical theory of homosexuality is a little diffuse and perhaps vague and inconclusive, but there is no doubt that progress into a deeper understanding and clarification of it has been and is being made. In his final word Fenichel heralds this by saying:

> Homosexuality has proved to be the product of specific mechanisms of *defence* which facilitate the persistence of the repression of both the Oedipus and castration complex. At the same time, the aim of homosexual object choice is the avoidance of emotions around the castration complex, which otherwise would disturb the sexual pleasure, or at least the attainment of reassurance against them.

Some modern psychoanalysts, particularly those of the Kleinian school, have carried the psychopathology of homosexuality a little deeper, namely right back to what is called the *oral* phase of libidinal development. Paula Heimann and Susan Isaacs (1952) say:

> The primary oral and anal anxieties are the chief factors in the homosexual fixation. . . . It is the anxiety stimulated by cannibalistic phantasies which is the most potent factor in oral fixation. . . . The dread of the destroyed internal object (devoured and therefore inside) can only be allayed by continued oral pleasure . . . it is this insatiable need which binds the libido to oral and anal forms. . . . We know that such fixations of the oral phase, with all its phantasies and anxieties, lead to profound disturbances of the genital function.

Good, as well as bad, reactive patterns also are apparently displaced from the oral zone to the genital:

It is now widely recognised that the earlier stages have definite and positive contributions to make to the genital phase. . . . Contributions from the oral phase strengthen genital impulses . . . the woman's genital impulses and phantasies take over her happy experiences at the breast. . . . It is not enough to say that there is a displacement of certain elements in the oral phase to the genital. This is true, but it is an incomplete statement. Those oral phantasies and aims have remained *uninterruptedly active* in the unconscious mind exerting a favourable influence and promoting genitality. The oral libido has remained labile enough to be transferred to the genital and satisfied there.

This is rather difficult material for the nonanalytical reader, especially "the dread of the destroyed internal object (devoured and therefore inside) . . . ." A brief explanation, even if inadequate, may be desirable.

Soon after the infant is born it begins to require something, some "object" in the outside world as a necessary aid to the gratification of its oral (and hunger) instinct. It may be assumed that previously instinct gratification was in a sense physiological or auto-erotic. Now it requires *something* in its mouth to suck; it has become dependent upon this object," and the process of feeding, to allay its oral desires and hunger. This libidinal stage is said in psychoanalysis to be one of *oral primacy*. The "object" which is utilised for gratification of its need is the breast or nipple. With this "object" it has established what may be called its first "object relationship." The point of importance is that *the pattern of its reactions to all subsequent object relationships is laid down by this first object relationship*. The external world, outside itself, when recognised as such, will tend to be *good* and *bad* in proportion to the relative amounts of gratification (pleasure) and frustration (pain) experienced orally at the breast.

The second point for consideration is the beginning of mental processes. The theory is that all sensory experiences are accompanied by what psychoanalysis calls *unconscious phantasy*. The baby knows of no world outside its sensory experiences, including the sensations of its frustrations. When oral gratification is temporarily frustrated, the infant tries to compensate for this by hallucinations of gratification. This is deduced from an observation of its sucking movements. Of course, this can provide only very temporary relief. If frustration is excessive appetite increases, the baby may become ravenous, and there is psychoanalytical evidence that it proceeds to unconscious phantasies appropriate to this ravenous condition. The phantasies include the devouring not only of the milk, but also of the breast and even subsequently of the mother! This is called "cannibalistic phantasy." Whatever the child feels and phantasies will, sooner or later, be *projected* and imagined to be the state of its external world also. That is to say, if its internal world is cannibalistic, it automatically assumes the existence of a cannibalistic world outside itself. This process of projection leads to fantastic fears. Thus the baby, like the wild animal, is said at this stage to live in a world of a desire to eat and a fear of being eaten.

Now, if this fantastic pattern of *object relationship* is greatly accentuated, for instance by undue oral stimulations and frustrations, the organism is apt to acquire both an undue degree of fixation to this oral phase and an undue degree of fear owing to projection of its oral hunger. Subsequently, when, in the course of development, this pattern of its first object relationship becomes inevitably *displaced* to successive zones of erotic primacy—finally to the genital zone—the object relationship at the last, or genital, zone becomes filled with the pattern acquired at the oral zone, including the unconscious phantasies and feelings of desire and *fear*. The unconscious phantasy may then include the fear of being devoured—by the vagina. This is probably the most important factor responsible for psycho-sexual impotence in men. Similar unconscious phantasies are responsible for fear of the penis and frigidity in women. A man with such an unconscious phantasy of the female genitals is liable to avoid intimate relationships with women, even to hate them, and for these reasons to be unconsciously on the defensive against any urges which might lead him towards the feared genitals. He commonly desires access to male genitals to reassure himself against his unconscious phantasies of castration associated with a female genital. He is thus predisposed to homosexuality.

Margaret Mead (1949) points out that among the peoples of the South Sea Islands those who do not wean their children early are of a placid and friendly disposition, whereas those who are in the habit of depriving the child of breast feeding are warlike, aggressive and unpleasant. Her testimony indicates at least a relationship between the oral phase and the genital pattern.

> Amongst the Arapesh, little girls share their mothers' extreme valuation of nursing, and are as unwilling as little boys to be weaned. In Manus, mothers have already communicated their lack of enthusiasm for the maternal role to their small daughters. . . . A Manus boy . . . will not grow up to be gentle and considerate as a lover." [For an Arapesh boy] rape and active homosexuality are outside his pattern.

Bergler (1948), like Fenichel and the Kleinians, emphasises especially, first, that homosexuality is the result of a *defensive* mechanism, and secondly, that what it is on the defensive against is the acute anxieties connected with *oral and cannibalistic phantasies* and therefore against aggressive and destructive (oral) urges. Strangely enough *heterosexuality* can itself be a defence against latent homosexual tendencies. That is to say, heterosexual behaviour in the so-called "bi-sexual" (to which category all persons *unconsciously* belong) can at least have a subsidiary function in helping to keep out of consciousness repressed and repudiated homosexual proclivities.

Many heterosexual persons, rightly so-called, are in part *potentially* homosexual without being able to admit to consciousness such a proclivity in themselves. Perhaps all normal persons, as Stekel says, belong more or less to this category. To illustrate what I mean, I can quote from my clinical material a patently heterosexual man who mentioned in the course of analysis, in association to thoughts of having a general massage, how he would hate to be massaged by a *man* as he said *for fear* that the experience might give him an erection. At the same time, this patient anticipates with pleasure the phantasy of being massaged by a *woman*. He says he would enjoy that, especially if it *did* give him an erection. The interpretation is of course that he would feel libidinal response to such attentions from either sex irrespectively, but with the important difference that his sexual response to the stimulations of a male would be resisted, repudiated, and *feared*, or at least he would be fearful of their exposure. On the other hand, his sexual response to the stimulations of a female would not be repudiated by his super-ego and ego, *not feared*, and therefore could be enjoyed. Thus the difference in the two cases would appear to

be more superficial than the sexual impulse itself. In the same
way that heterosexuality can help in one's normal defences
against homosexual proclivities, so homosexuality can be a defence against feared and therefore repressed heterosexual impulses. In each case an essential function is that of allaying anxiety.

Bergler reminds us how important are the repressed anxieties in connection with pre-Oedipus, oral, cannibalistic
phantasies, as a basic psychological factor in the fear of the
female genital. The Oedipus conflict is, of course, a later development. The emotional patterns elaborated in the object-
relationships of the Oedipus complex enter into the defences
against both heterosexuality and homosexuality. The point
is that both the emotional nature and intensity of the Oedipus
phantasies are determined by the earlier repressed oral phantasies, with their attendant anxieties in the unconscious. These
anxieties lead to heterosexual impotence and to the homosexual
defence against heterosexuality and, secondarily, against a
recognition of the impotence. The conscious or remembered
relationships to parents are, of course, merely more superficial
aspects of these unconscious patterns which were determined
at such a very much earlier stage of development.

Thus emotional reactions to parents, parent fixation to
either sex and by either sex, are merely later expressions of
more deeply unconscious psychic structure. They are another
intermediate stage, in turn determining relationships to persons
outside the family, and the choice of which sex is chosen for
those relationships. What is quite inadequately appreciated
by almost all of us is that, apart from overt sexual behaviour,
some stimulation of unconscious sexual phantasy is an accompaniment of practically all our human relationships.

Overt sexual behaviour is merely the implementation by action, often crude and inaccurate, of all sorts and every shade of subtle emotional interaction of one person on another. Apart from the reversal of roles from active to passive, and vice versa, that commonly takes place in homosexual relationships, hetero- sexual persons are constantly reacting similarly to each other, unconsciously or consciously angling and fencing for emo- tional advantage in their mutual relationships. This is par- ticularly true of married couples. Commonly they share out, or divide, their respective active or "masculine" roles, the husband normally assuming the more dominant position in the sexual sphere and the wife in the domestic and compensatory spheres. If the husband is psychologically inadequate as a sexually dominating male, we commonly see the wife becom- ing more assertive and masculine, even proceeding as it were to "emasculate" him further, and assume his role—acting, in an obscure way, much as the passive homosexual may when he becomes active towards his weakening partner.

In other words, the active-passive, masculine-feminine re- lationship of one person to another is operative with subtle grades of variation, and even reversal, in the unconscious, and, in one person's emotional repercussions upon another, quite apart from overt sexual implementation. It forms the basis of inter-personal relationships.

Positions of subordination to other males (or females) on a social plane have their repercussion upon our unconscious feminine component, or upon our defences, in the same way that positions of power are stimulating to masculine elements within us, and effect our sexuality whether we know it or not. In short, homosexuality is unavoidable in the unconscious, however much it may be repudiated at conscious levels. Indeed, it may well be that the holding together of our social structure depends upon these very repudiated "bi-sexual" potentialities within the psyche. The stone which the builders rejected . . . from consciousness . . . ! What is inhibited sexually and even hidden from consciousness in civilised human beings may be apparent and overt in the behaviour of animals. Dr. Hamilton (1936) seems to suggest this through a biological approach. He says, with regard to social behaviour in monkeys, the immature female "is sufficiently bi-sexual to be capable of offering herself for copulation to hostile females at any age whenever there is a defensive need for doing so. . . . The readiness of the adult female to accept an invitation to play the role of copulating male, when she has directed a hostile attack against a fellow of either sex, again discloses the adaptive value of retained 'bi-sexuality', since it is in the interests of both individual and species survival." Dr. Zuckermann in his *Sexual Life of Monkeys* describes how the lesser male constantly saves itself from destruction by "presenting" itself sexually to the angry "overlord." This gesture almost invariably stops the attack, whether the invitation is accepted or not. It would thus seem that the capacity for "bi-sexuality" or homosexuality is an essential ingredient in survival of the individual and of the monkey society. Dr. Hamilton goes on to say: "If, as can be indubitably established by appropriate methods of experimentation, homosexual behaviour is at times resorted to as a purely defensive measure by the infra-human primate, a question arises as to whether defensiveness is a factor in the determination of human homosexuality." On the basis of my own clinical experience, while not being able to quote cases of overt practice of homosexuality as a defensive measure, I can vouch for its unconscious equivalent being very active in every department of human relationship. Therefore I have no doubt that it does actually happen. I think at the moment of a capable male patient who cannot be employed because he unconsciously equates subordination to an employer with the homosexual passive attitude; it stimulates the affects of an unconscious phantasy of emasculation and being used as a female, and therefore provokes aggressive reactions in him. In other words, it is his defences against homosexuality which make him unemployable. This is merely a sample of the sort of thing that is going on unrecognised in the relationships of one person to another.

In accordance with psychoanalytical evidence and my own clinical experience, I am convinced that our behaviour, our compulsions, and even our beliefs, emanate from unconscious phantasies, with their emotional patterns, inherited, and acquired in infancy. Hence our *understanding* of homosexuality will never be arrived at by statistical, or conscious-level enquiry, but will be achieved only through knowledge of the unconscious phantasies revealed through deep personal analysis. The causes of the manifold effects lie within the individual's unconscious mind. Perhaps the truth is that no amount of experience will provide us with a complete answer to the riddle in the terms in which we seek it. This is because the problem, as ordinarily presented, is incorrectly formulated. Nevertheless, experience is of value. I think it will lead us to a reorientation and a more correct formulation of the nature of the mind, of instincts, emotions and sexuality, and with this of the etiology of hidden and overt homosexuality; and, of what may prove to be of greater practical importance, the psychopathology of our often stupid and morbid and injurious reactions against it.

The unconscious naturally contains every phantasy however fantastic, everything we can possibly think of and a great deal more that we cannot think of or cannot believe. This is because our mental censorship will not permit us to do so. Behaviour, all sexual behaviour, is merely a question of which of these innumerable sexual phantasies eludes the censorship, the internal unconscious mental censorship, and emerges in thought or in action. Anything, everything is possible, as can be proved by the fact that anything and everything *does* actually occur—including incredibly savage reactions against the repressed impulses, or rather against those who manifest them. We are none of us fundamentally different from one another. Analysis shows that all persons, normal as well as neurotic and homosexual, have an infinite variety of phantasies in their unconscious, and that these phantasies are the source from which spring their feelings, moods, thoughts and behaviour. The apparent differences between us do not lie so much in the differences in our unconscious phantasies, for as I have said, we all have similar unconscious phantasies, though admittedly of different degrees of intensity. The apparent differences between one person and another lie mainly in something relatively superficial, a defensive mechanism that depends more upon the nature and intensity of the repressing forces (censorship and super-ego) than upon the nature and intensity of the impulses which they are repressing. In short, what emerges into consciousness or into action is the outcome of the conflict between super-ego and instinctual pressure. The ego may attach itself to one or other of these antagonists, but it is commonly buffeted about from one side to the other in the course of the conflict, and always in varying proportions divided or split between them. In any case, the outcome commonly depends to a lesser degree than we suppose upon the part the ego plays, though it is usually more on the side of the repressing forces. The trouble, if trouble there be, lies in the degree to which the relatively feeble ego is overwhelmed by the strength of the forces on one side or the other.

With most so-called normal people, it may be that the ego is more frequently overwhelmed by super-ego forces, resulting in harsh or sadistic reaction formations, instigated by our own intrapsychic insecurity and consequent fear of the repressed. In this field, reaction formations are commonly too severe to be borne by oneself, and are, therefore, projected on to a scapegoat, resulting in punishments being practically always worse, or causing more misery, than the crime. We find in the course of our analysis that denials, particularly emotionally charged denials, show the existence in the unconscious of that which is denied. In the same way that there is every variety of erotic and fetishistic mania of active and passive homosexuality and perversion, there is similarly every variety and degree of antipathy. Indeed, the latter is but the denial and repression of the former. It may be said that the antipathies, being more characteristic of the super-ego, however aggressive and destructive, are generally more freely revealed, and even advertised, than are the impulses and mania which they deny. Few people would display their perversions with the freedom and readiness with which they exhibit their moral prejudices, not suspecting that the latter prove beyond doubt the (repressed) existence within them of the former. Behaviour itself emerges only after an unconscious struggle.

The behaviouristic *form* sexuality takes (*e.g.* homosexuality) may be compared to the manifest content of a dream, or the appearance of a symptom. All these manifestations are merely the end product of innumerable determinants, some of which (like the latent content of the dream from which the manifest content emerges) may be very different indeed from the manifest form. Indeed, the main determinant for a manifestation may be, and often is, the diametrical opposite to that which is expressed; the manifest symptom may contain more denial than exhibition of its chief determinant. It may be a reversal for the purpose of defence, disguise or denial. Civilisation is a denial of the savage within. Polite social conduct, our *mores*, is a denial of aggression and of sexuality. At best, our manifest behaviour contains more resisting or repressing forces; at worst, it may appear to concern itself with these alone. Thus manifest homosexuality may be *essentially* a denial (unconsciously determined) of heterosexuality. I am convinced that it is sometimes, though much more rarely than the converse situation, nothing more or less than just this. A factor determining this proclivity is often excessive fear of the uncontrollable power of the repressed heterosexual urges. As we see when we expose the transference during an analysis, in the unconscious it would be as though, at all costs, incest with mother must be prevented and denied. This is because it is associated with rebellion, murder and destruction, and, at an oral level, with cannibalism and the fear of being eaten. Ernest Jones (1912) says: "The central content of the repressed impulses may be summed up in two words: incest and murder."

Beliefs and behaviour are merely *expressions* of the various ingredients of unconscious phantasies and conflicts. No behaviour is amazing, incredible or mysterious, for in the unconscious we are accustomed to finding every ingredient, conceivable and inconceivable. Indeed, "inconceivable" merely means repressed from consciousness. The canon of all science, cause and effect, operates just as truly and implacably in the psychological sphere as in every other, and this holds as true of the repressive reactions to instinctual behaviour as it does of this behaviour itself. I allude to the fact that whereas some persons express their emotional pressure in various forms of instinctual behaviour, and whereas others, repressing these impulses, suffer from a consequent or accompanying neurosis, still other persons, perhaps the most "normal," express the super-ego side of their conflict in even more cruel intolerances and destructive reactions. The latter forms of expression are often designated as righteous indignation or even as justice and punishment. They commonly have no more reality basis or justification than the former. Homosexuals can be just as intolerant of heterosexuality as heterosexuals of homosexuality . . . and paranoiacs of everything. Such intolerances only show that each has specialised in his own particular form of defence against the opposite tendencies within himself. Stekel says: "The heterosexual is inspired with disgust at any homosexual acts. That proves his affectively determined negative attitude. For disgust is but the obverse of attraction. The homosexual manifests the same feeling of disgust for woman." From a sociological standpoint it could be argued, though maybe in Machiavellian fashion, that if unlimited expansion of homosexuality could destroy the human race through lack of population, heterosexuality may destroy it by excess of population—which latter, incidentally, is the greatest human problem.

From the point of view of a scientific study of nature it should be remembered that although homosexuality is prevalent in all mammals, and, indeed, in all living organisms, it is never in excess of heterosexuality. To imagine that laws or penalties could put an end to it is evidently to place man-made laws above those of nature. It may be that we might as well, in the fashion of King Canute, make laws forbidding the tide to come in from the sea. From a legislative point of view it should be recognised that we are dealing with *two* psychological conditions. One is homosexuality and the other is a reaction of horror against it. Each may express itself behaviouristically, the first in the phenomenon of homosexual activity, and the second in the phenomenon of senseless prohibition, often with savage penalties. I fancy that the second phenomenon is more serious than the first, and even more morbid. Unlike the first, however, the second phenomenon *may* be remediable through the medium of replacing ignorance by knowledge and a proper assessment of the facts, and an understanding that nature's ways have not destroyed our species and are in no danger of doing so. Knowledge and understanding may do more than this; it may enable us to prevent or limit the development of homosexual tendencies—for example, by ceasing excessive frustration of heterosexual tendencies when these are developmentally ripe. Kinsey (1953) says: "We are inclined to believe that moral restraint of pre-marital heterosexual activity is the most important single factor contributing to the development of a homosexual history."

Those who would abolish homosexuality please note that even statistics incline the investigator to believe that this restraint is *"the most important single factor."* Reich (1942) wrote: "The alternative . . . is not: *sexuality* or *abstinence;* but: *natural and healthy,* or *perverse and neurotic sexual life."*

It seems to me that law-makers should be careful to confine themselves to their very proper concern for social and individual welfare, and should be particularly careful to exclude from the legal code *unnecessary* interferences with the liberty of the individual lest with this denial they prevent or destroy necessary adjustments—or worse—and give expression merely to emotional prejudice and their morbid anxiety or personal gratification, without serving any useful purpose. Homosexuality is not necessarily a crime against the person any more than is heterosexuality, *but* assault, rape or violence *are* crimes against the person, irrespective of whether they be homosexual or heterosexual, or asexual. The law as it exists on all matters of this nature leads to a lot of indirect, as well as direct, useless misery. I shall never forget the homosexual lawyer who was once a patient of mine whose defence against his own (recognised) tendencies to homosexuality and sadism was to "sublimate" them into a professional zeal in prosecuting and persecuting homosexuals. He was prosecuting his own guilt *in others*, and earning his living by so doing. Was this a sublimation or the perversion of a perversion?

Dr. Clifford Allen says:

> Henry and Gross draw attention to the fact that the homosexual lives in fear of being blackmailed. His mind is so perpetually haunted by the thought of falling into the hands of the authorities that he is an easy subject for the blackmailer. We have pointed out that homosexuals may be driven to violence by threat of exposure.

The only proper approach to this problem is knowledge— knowledge of the facts and understanding. Emotional reactions are morbid symptoms whether they manifest themselves in the positive acts of perversions, such as homosexuality, or in the reactive forms of rage and sadistic punishment *against* perversions and homosexuality. Both perversions and emotional reactions against them are symptoms. *Symptoms are not appropriate therapeutic agents, nor are they sound judgment.*

Scientific approach demands knowledge; nothing is achieved by an ostrich policy of ignorance, nor by emotional biases of a positive or negative nature. Nobody should be permitted to judge or to punish or to prescribe treatment until he has not only read and understood the literature on the subject, but what is far more important, until he has read and understood the "book" of his own repressed and unconscious conflicts. That is to say, until he has submitted himself to a personal analysis and become fully aware of the repressed and denied homosexuality within himself. "He that is without sin among you, let him cast a stone." A denial of "sin" on a conscious plane is evidence of nothing more than denial. Analysis reveals that everyone is perjurer as well as sinner!

The unrealistic attitude of the law on homosexuality can apparently be demonstrated by statistical evidence, apart from psychological exposition. After telling us that thirty-seven per cent of the male population has some homosexual experience, and the surprising fact that "seventeen per cent of the farm boys have animal intercourse," Kinsey, by the simple process of adding percentages, concludes:

> All of these, and still other types of sexual behaviour are illicit activities, each performance of which is punishable as a crime under the law. The persons involved in these activities, taken as a whole, constitute more than ninety-five per cent of the total male population . . . It is the total ninety-five per cent of the male population for which the judge, or board of public safety, or church, or civic group demands apprehension, arrest, and conviction, when they call for a clean-up of the sex offenders in a community. *It is, in fine, a proposal that five per cent of the population should support the other ninety-five per cent in penal institutions!*" (My italics)

Legal attitudes, like most human belief and behaviour—like homosexuality itself—may thus be seen to be more emotionally determined (*i.e.* letting out the tension of those unconscious conflicts) than realistic.

In conclusion, I should like to summarise a personal theory regarding this vexed question of the alleged antithesis between the hypotheses of congenital and acquired factors in the causation of homosexuality, and, for that matter, in the etiology of all other reactive patterns, behaviour and belief. My theory, which I have worked out much more fully than here suggested, is that the antithesis is illusionary and is due to the mistake, fostered by the current, and to my mind erroneous, attitude of biologists, of assuming that old instincts alone are inherited and that acquired patterns of behaviour, however long established, are not. They regard life as beginning anew with each individual birth, instead of regarding it as the continuity which, to me, it obviously is.

I will begin with a little story merely to *illustrate* my theory. When I was in the London Zoo recently, a young tiger in an outside cage suddenly, for no reason that I could see, became extremely excited, crouching and weaving as though getting ready to spring, with eyes fixed upon some object beyond me. Turning around I saw a baby elephant in the distance being led through the grounds by a keeper. The tiger had not shown any such excitement at the presence of human children or of any other animals, and, knowing that it came from the Bengal jungle where tigers do occasionally prey upon young elephants, I assumed at first that it must itself, at some period of its jungle career, have killed and tasted a baby elephant. However, on reading the plaque on its cage I learned

that not it, but only its parents, had been captured in the
Bengal jungle. This particular young tiger had been born in
captivity in the Whipsnade Zoo! There is no doubt that given
the opportunity it would have followed the behaviour of its
ancestors in selecting for its prey the somewhat unusual diet of
baby elephant. The flavour of baby elephant resided presumably in its constitutional (inherited) reactive pattern.

Can we draw a line and say *when* an acquired pattern of
behaviour becomes inheritable like an "instinct?" The biologists say "never." Yet I am convinced that my own experience
as a scientist and an analyst tell me differently.

Perhaps this "dogma" of current biology is the worthy suc-
cessor of its previous die-hard dogma of the immutability of
species, and even of their separate creation. Almost a hundred
year ago (1859), Darwin began his revolutionary work, *The
Origin of Species* with the following words: "The great majority of naturalists believe that species are immutable produc-
tions, and have been separately created."

I am convinced that instincts, *like species*, were not created
separately—not even by the indirect independent-of-environ-
ment or magical process of mutations. Throughout the individual's life, instincts are being modified, however slightly, and
new reactive patterns are being formed. This is a process of
reactive adaptation to environment, and I am convinced that
this is the process whereby new adaptations, new adaptations
of old instincts *and the evolution of new instincts*, are in process of being brought about, however gradually and imper-
ceptibly, throughout the ages. I am convinced that this is not
just simply a question of acquired reactions in antithesis to inherited ones; this is *how* the inherited ones were originally
acquired and how fresh patterns of reaction are being acquired

and new modifications and new instincts evolved. To my mind *this* is evolution and every other concept of it makes nonsense. Processes other than adaptation to environment can be no more than subsidiary to this main determinant. Otherwise life and environment *would not fit together;* life, and evolution, would be impossible.

Thus my contention is that the current etiological antithesis between inherited and acquired is no antithesis at all, and is created purely out of a misconception as to how all behaviouristic reactions, all instincts, are formed. Congenital and environmental, inherited and acquired, are to my mind only different terms for the same process of reactive adaptations to environment. They differ only in regard to the Time when the adaptation took place and the Depth of the modification in the mind or body. That body and that mind is a continuum hereditarily, only apparently, but not actually, broken by the phenomenon of reproduction with its Mendelian laws of averages. Hence my conclusion is that the argument about whether homosexuality is congenital *or* acquired is based on a misconception. The truth is that "congenital" and "acquired" are merely different operational stages of the self-same process, and the one has no meaning without the other. Thus, I am convinced that homosexuality, *like everything else*, is *both* congenital *and* acquired, with relative quantitative variations of each etiological factor.

ALLEN, CLIFFORD   *The Sexual Perversions and Abnormalities.*
London: Oxford University Press, 1940.

BERG, CHARLES   *The First Interview with a Psychiatrist.* London: Allen & Unwin, 1955.

BERGLER, EDMUND   "Homosexuality and the Kinsey Report,"
The Homosexuals. New York: The Citadel Press, 1954.

CAPRIO, FRANK S.   *Female Homosexuality.* New York: The Citadel Press, 1954.

ELLIS, HAVELOCK   *Studies in the Psychology of Sex.* Volume
II, "Sexual Inversion." Philadelphia: F. A. Davis Company,
1901, Revised edition 1926.

FENICHEL, OTTO   *The Psychoanalytic Theory of Neurosis.*
London: Kegan Paul, Trench, Trubner & Co. Ltd., 1946.

FERENCZI, SANDOR   *On the Nosology of Male Homosexuality
(Homoeroticism).* Reprinted in *Contributions of Psycho-
Analysis.* Boston: Richard Badger, Gorham Press, 1916.

FREUD, S.   *Three Essays on the Theory of Sexuality.* (1905)
First English Edition 1949. London: Imago Publishing
Company Ltd.

FREUD, S.   *Leonardo da Vinci* (1916). English Edition 1922.
London: Kegan Paul, Trench, Trubner & Co. Ltd.

HAMILTON, GILBERT VAN TASSEL   "Incest and Homosexuality" from *Encyclopedia Sexualis.* U.S.A.: Dingwall-Rock
Ltd., 1936.

HIRSCHFELD, MAGNUS *Sexual Anomalies and Perversions* (1938). New and Revised Edition. London: Encyclopaedic Press, reprint 1953.

JENKINS, M. *Genetic Psychological Monographs*, 3, 1928.

JONNES, ERNEST *Papers on Psycho-Analysis*, 1912. London: Baillière, Tindall and Cox, 1948.

KALLMANN, FRANZ "Comparative Twin Study on the Genetic Aspects of Male Homosexuality." New York: *J. Nerv. Ment. Dis.* pp. 115, 283–298; 1952.

KINSEY, ALFRED C. *Sexual Behavior in the Human Male.* Philadelphia and London: W. B. Saunders Company, 1948.

KINSEY, ALFRED C. *Sexual Behavior in the Human Female.* Philadelphia and London: W. B. Saunders Company, 1953.

KLEIN, MELANIE; HEIMANN, PAULA; ISAACS, SUSAN; RIVIERE, JOAN *Developments in Psycho-Analysis.* London: The Hogarth Press Ltd., 1952.

KRICH, A. M. *The Homosexuals.* New York: The Citadel Press, 1954.

LANG, T. "Genetic Determination of Homosexuality." *J. Nerv. Ment. Dis.* 92.55; 1940.

MALINOWSKI *Sexual Life of Savages*, 1929.

MAYER-GROSS, WILLIAM; SLATER, ELIOT; ROTH, MARTIN *Clinical Psychiatry.* London: Cassell & Co. Ltd., 1954.

MEAD, MARGARET *Male and Female.* London: Victor Gollancz Ltd., 1949.

MYERSON, A. NEUSTADT, R. *Bisexuality and Male Homosexuality*, 1942.

REICH, WILHELM *The Function of the Orgasm.* New York: Orgone Institute Press, 1942.

ROLPH, C. H. *Women of the Streets.* Edited by C. H. Rolph

on behalf of the British Social Biology Council. London: Secker & Warburg, 1955.

STEKEL, WILLIAM *Bisexual Love.* Translated by J. S. Van Teslaar. Boston: Richard Badger, Emerson Books Inc., 1922.

THOMPSON, DR. CLARA *A Study of Interpersonal Relations.* U.S.A.: Hermitage Press Inc., 1949.

ZUCKERMANN *Sexual Life of Monkeys.* London: Kegan Paul, Trench, Trubner & Co. Ltd., 1932.

THE WOLFENDEN REPORT: DISCUSSION AND CRITICISM

by Charles Berg, M.D.

In Great Britain, on August 4, 1954, a Committee was appointed by the Government to submit a report on the law and practice relating to homosexual offences, and prostitution. In the case of homosexuality the assignment was somewhat different, as the Committee was asked at the same time to consider the *treatment* of persons convicted of such offences by the courts. This did not apply to heterosexual prostitution, which in any case does not concern us in this book.

The Chairman was Sir John Wolfenden, Vice-Chancellor of Reading University, and the fifteen members included two judges of the High Court, three women, two Members of Parliament, two doctors, two lawyers and two ministers of religion.

This Committee presented its report in September, 1957, after sixty-two meetings, more than half of which were devoted to the oral examination of "witnesses." It was careful to point out that its terms of reference were concerned throughout with the *law*, and offences against it, with what were the essential elements of a criminal offence, based upon the moral, social and cultural standards of society, law and public opinion, rather than on the psychological factors responsible for a particular form of behaviour. In other words, the emphasis was upon the overt or avowed (or pretended) psychology of the public (public opinion), as expressed in law, and not upon the psychopathology of the offender or the offence.

Nevertheless, in the course of their investigations, the Committee naturally found it unavoidable to examine certain aspects of the psychology of homosexuality, although these aspects of its investigation are not officially emphasised in its report. For instance, it declares that it found it important to make a clear distinction between "homosexuality" and "homosexual offences." It says (page 11 of the Report):

> There is a further problem how widely the description "homosexual" should be applied. According to the psychoanalytic school, a homosexual component (sometimes conscious, often not) exists in everybody; and if this is correct homosexuality in this sense is universal. Without going so far as to accept this view *in toto*, it is possible to realise that the issue of latent homosexuality . . . is relevant to any assessment of the frequency of occurrence of the condition of homosexuality.

Naturally it was not long before the Committee, consisting largely of lawyers, J.P.'s, M.P.'s and clergy, obviously found itself in difficulties. These difficulties remained or increased throughout its deliberations, and had something to do with the resignations of two of its members, and the reservations of about half the remainder. Their difficulties, with emphasis on their task of defining what was or was not a crime, legal meanings and legal sanctions and punishments, naturally led to the familiar juridical preoccupation of hair-splitting, particularly in regard to the meanings of words—was homosexuality a "disease" or was it not a "disease"—and such irrelevant speculations, tending to ignore (but not altogether) what one would have thought to be the essential need to find out everything about it, including particularly its *meaning*, its psycho-pathology and its etiology. (It is noteworthy that there was not one psychoanalyst on the Committee). As they were of course unaware of the meaning, psychopathology and etiology of *their own* attitudes, defensive mechanisms, and biases, it is inevitable that they should get into increasing difficulties. By the time we have examined their work, we may come to the conclusion that *all* of them should have resigned. However, within their limitations they are intelligent, well-educated people, and are honestly doing their best to integrate, explain and to make "recommendations" in connection with a phenomenon which they are, by nature of the unanalysed, civilisation-indoctrinated mind, incapable of understanding.

Most reviewers of the Wolfenden Report seem to have started at the end, rushing into a recital of the "recommendations" before considering the process of arriving at these recommendations. The most revolutionary and "controversial" of these "recommendations" is that "homosexual behaviour between consenting adults in private be no longer a criminal offence." (The age of consent is specified as twenty-one years.) It took a great deal of discussion regarding the differentiation between "private sin" and "the business of the law" to pass this recommendation, and it may be noted that one member of the Committee, Mr. Adair, took great pains to dissociate himself from it, writing six closely printed pages (pages 117–123) to justify his disagreement. To the credit of the Committee, the majority of its members emphasised (paragraph 61):

> . . . the importance which society and the law ought to give to individual freedom of choice and action in matters of private morality. Unless a deliberate attempt is to be made by society, acting through the agency of the law, to equate the

sphere of crime with that of sin, there must remain a realm of private morality and immorality which is, in brief and crude terms, not the law's business. To say this is not to condone or encourage private immorality. On the contrary, to emphasise the personal and private nature of moral or immoral conduct is to emphasise the personal and private responsibility of the individual for his own actions, and that is a responsibility which a mature agent can properly be expected to carry for himself without the threat of punishment from the law.

Of this and many of the observations in this Report, we may say that the reasoning and breadth of view are commendable. I can only add that it is a pity the Committee did not extend the reasoning above quoted to the entire subject of the punishment for homosexual acts which are free from any element of *assault* (a separate crime), in which case a great step forward could have been made. For instance, the law should be concerned with safeguarding the liberty of the individual, quite irrespective of whether this liberty is infringed upon by threats, blackmail, robbery, unwanted interference, assault, decent or indecent, heterosexual or homosexual. If the law is going to act other than according to these principles, it itself is exercising an unwarranted interference with the liberty of the individual, and is therefore no doubt quite justly regarded by many of its victims as the criminal.

I remember the case of a trembling, sweating, little man in the forties, who was brought to me by another homosexual on account of his incapacity, owing to his neurotic anxiety state. The first story he told me was that ten years ago in a darkened car, well off the road and hidden among the trees of Epping Forest, he was "spooning" with a man friend, a little older than himself. Suddenly all the doors were flung open and the interior of the car was illuminated by powerful flashlights. Both men were arrested and finally, after they had been induced to incriminate many other persons, received five years' imprisonment each.

The point of this story is that so far as this man's psychology was concerned, he could no more see the wrong, let alone the "criminality," of "spooning" with his man friend in what he considered to be privacy, than the average heterosexual man could see in "spooning" with his girl friend, fiancée, or for that matter, wife. After all, this was his sexual pattern, and he had been living according to it in greater or lesser degrees for the whole of his life.

However, he was not very strong-minded, and the action of the law had greatly shaken him, even to the extent of causing him to wonder whether his whole concept of morality was entirely "off the rails." In psychological language one may say that the firm and confident action of the law had so stimulated his superego that he had been overwhelmed with fear of *it*, that is to say, with guilt feelings and anxiety. It had caused him to brood, and later on to feel that five years' imprisonment was not enough, and that he deserved the extreme penalty. Indeed, since his arrest he had been near to suicide on several occasions, the last one of which would have been successful had it not been for the timely intrusion of the kind homosexual friend who had brought him to consult me.

The recommendation that homosexual behaviour between consenting adults in private no longer be a criminal offence is broached as early as Section 62 in the Report, and is singled out as the first of the recommendations under Section 355. None of the other recommendations is revolutionary. Further recommendations of comparatively minor interest include:

No. (xii), which urges that the prosecution of any homo-sexual offence more than twelve months old be barred by statute. This is watered down, however, by the qualification, "except for indecent assaults."

No. (vi) of Section 355, providing that no proceedings should be taken in respect of any homosexual act (other than an indecent assault) committed in private by a person *under twenty-one*, except by the Director of Public Prosecutions, or with the sanction of the Attorney-General.

No. (vi), suggesting that the term "brothel" include prem-ises used for homosexual practices.

The only remaining recommendation of the eighteen listed which seems to me to deserve any attention is number (vii), "that there be introduced revised maximum penalties in re-spect of buggery, gross indecency and indecent assaults." These are discussed under paragraph 90 and 91, and consist in general of an increase of the existing already fantastic severity of the punishments. For instance (para. 91 (c)): "Gross indecency committed by a man over twenty-one with a person of or above the age of sixteen but below the age of twenty-one, in circumstances not amounting to an indecent assault . . .", the suggested maximum penalty for this is increased to five years' imprisonment. According to paragraph 92, this is designed to protect the young (i.e., those between sixteen and twenty-one) because of "the danger of emotional or psychological damage."

However, before coming to a discussion of the "final rec-ommendations," let us go through the Report more systemati-cally, though I shall have to be extremely brief to avoid tedium since so much that the Committee has to say consists of little more than platitudes. They ask (paragraph 13), "What are the

essential elements of a criminal offence?" and admit an inability to answer the question. Nevertheless, this does not prevent them from muddling through on their "own formulation." This includes providing for "sufficient safeguards
against exploitation and corruption of others, particularly
those who are specially vulnerable." One cannot disagree, but
is tempted to reflect that such persons are always taken advantage of in every walk of life, one way or another, hence the
worthy task may prove impossible. The strong arm of father
or mother is often the only safeguard.

Law, regarded as a means of leading and fortifying public
opinion (paragraph 16), creates difficulties, as the Committee
found it impossible to discover "an unequivocal 'public opinion,' and we have felt bound to try to reach conclusions for
ourselves." In other words, according to their own pro- or
anti-emotionally determined biases.

The Committee discovered (paragraph 22) that homosexuality is not an " 'all or none' condition, . . . All gradations can
exist from apparently exclusive homosexuality . . . to apparently
exclusive heterosexuality." They add, "though in the latter case
there may be transient and minor homosexual inclinations, for
instance in adolescence." Nevertheless this Committee of fifteen (or thirteen) learned men and women is apparently too
nervous or too weak to demand any alteration in the existing
criminal law, which would send the unfortunate victim of one
of these "transient and minor homosexual inclinations" to a
long term of imprisonment, or worse. To the analyst it is well
known that some persons reach "adolescence" comparatively
late in life, and indeed some appear never to grow out of it.
The Committee agrees "that a transient homosexual phase in
development is very common and should usually cause neither

surprise or concern." But three years in prison probably will!

It was found on statistical investigation that a large group of homosexuals averaged fifteen criminal acts a year each. According to this, the ratio of undiscovered criminal acts to those discovered by the police would be about 2,500 to 1. This rockets to the skies in the Kinsey findings that within the age-group twenty-one to thirty the ratio is 30,000 to 1. In the light of this it would seem that legal sanctions are somewhat irrelevant to the whole issue. The issue would naturally be security from detection, and this makes the barbarous severity of the punishments imposed upon that unfortunate one in 30,000 who is detected all the more preposterous. Perhaps what would be relevant here is a psychological investigation of the source of all this pretence or denial. The Wolfenden Committee does not bring out these matters.

It sounds almost as though the Wolfenden Committee said very sympathetically: "Yes, we know, we know all about it. We know that everyone has homosexual potentialities within him or her, (though we do not propose to admit it). We know also that something like thirty thousand illegal homosexual acts are committed to every one that is discovered. Nevertheless we propose to allow the law (long since divergent from modern enlightenment) to continue to inflict every penalty short of death for that one in thirty thousand acts which is discovered, while the undiscovered 29,999 go scot-free, usually because neither party felt he had anything to complain about . . . or realized that it was as much his doing as the other person's."

While so non-committal in regard to ferocity of punishment and apparently not doubting its justification and validity, and even in some instances actually recommending an ex-

tension of the heaviest penalties (see paragraphs 91 and 92),
it is interesting that the Committee is only too ready to accept
unproven theories if they help to clarify its erroneous concep-
tions. For instance, they readily assimilate Dr. Kinsey's for-
mula of "homosexual-heterosexual continuum on a 7-point
scale, with a rating of 6 for sexual arousal and activity with
other males only, 3 for arousals and acts equally with either sex,
0 for exclusive heterosexuality, and intermediate ratings ac-
cordingly. The recognition of the existence of this continuum
is, in our opinion, important for two reasons. First, it leads to the
conclusion that homosexuals cannot reasonably be regarded as
quite separate from the rest of mankind. Secondly, as will be
discussed later, it has some relevance in connection with claims
made for the success of various forms of treatment."

Perhaps what is so misleading about the Kinsey seven-point
scale is that such a very large proportion of males belong, apart
from pubertal and adolescent inclinations, to the 0 category
(exclusive heterosexuality) and so large a proportion of the
remaining four or five per cent belong exclusively to the number 6 category (activity with other males only). The few
drifters towards whom Kinsey draws such unmerited attention may nevertheless be useful in so far as they demonstrate
the possibilities of flux and its relationship to development.

I think there is a much-needed tempering half-truth in this
unproven theory, in spite of its being misleading. Some psychoanalysts will have absolutely nothing to do with it. On the
other hand it does speak a truth about the *unconscious*, if a misleading part-"truth" about the actual sexual *behaviour* of persons upon which diagnosis is based. But here it should be remembered that some heterosexuals can behave homosexually—

or pretend—and some homosexuals can behave heterosexually without any change in their true sexual pattern.

If the Wolfenden Committee is so ready to accept even the doubtful theories of Dr. Kinsey (presumably because they make thinking easier), may I ask why they steer clear of some of his best-proven statistical theories? For example, after telling us that thirty-seven per cent of the male population has some homosexual experience in the course of their lives, and the surprising fact that "seventeen per cent of the farm boys have animal intercourse," Kinsey (1948), by the simple process of adding percentages, (and mathematics is usually regarded as infallible), concludes:

> All of these, and still other types of sexual behaviour are illicit activities, each performance of which is punishable as a crime under the law. The persons involved in these activities, taken as a whole, constitute more than ninety-five per cent of the total male population . . . It is the total ninety-five per cent of the male population for which the judge, or board of public safety, or church, or civic group demands apprehension, arrest, and conviction, when they call for a clean-up of the sex offenders in a community. *It is, in fine, a proposal that five per cent of the population should support the other ninety-five per cent in penal institutions!* (My italics).
> I refer to this again later.

If the Wolfenden Committee had got as far as acceptance of this exposition of the late Dr. Kinsey, they would of course have had no alternative but to pack up and go home, and have nothing more to do with this bogy-hunting nonsense, bogies which they cannot catch in any case . . . because they *are* bogies.

But perhaps we should give credit to these new arrivals into what to most of them must be a strange field of science, in that they manage to recognise a few well-worn truths, though it is more difficult to forgive their platitudinous expression of these. For instance, they recognise that (paragraph 24) "there are some in whom a latent homosexuality provides the motivation for activities of the greatest value to society. Examples of this are to be found among teachers, clergy, nurses, and those who are interested in youth movements and the care of the aged."

Nevertheless it would seem that this Committee would support a law which sentences one of these invaluable teachers, a teacher with a heaven-sent aptitude for the education of boys, to no less than life imprisonment for one slip from his sublimation to the instinctual source from which it springs.

Another truth which they appear to recognise, this time even in the face of considerable medical opposition, is that the fully established practising male homosexual will never be turned into a heterosexual person. One can say that he may be taught, or teach himself, to do the tricks, but very soon it will be revealed that they are only tricks without substance behind them, and he will find himself totally impotent—except with males. As the *British Medical Journal* of September 14, 1957, reports, quoting Drs. D. Curran and J. Whitby's contribution to the Wolfenden Report, "the most likely and valuable effects of treatment will be helping the young man whose homosexuality is transient but who requires psychotherapy to help him past it. For the patient who is adjusted to being homosexual much less is possible; *no doctor could produce for the committee a 'cured' case of complete homosexuality.*" (My italics.)

The *Journal* goes on to say, "The Committee stresses the need for planned research into all aspects of this problem, a view that every doctor will endorse." Indeed, they do stress it (paragraph 216). They recommend in their chapter on preventive measures and research "a research unit which would include, for example, psychiatrists, geneticists, endocrinologists, psychologists, criminologists, and statisticians." It does not mention who is going to pay all these highly skilled workers, and it does not mention that this is the sort of research that is going on in the course of all the trainings and treatments in every analytical consulting room, institution of psychotherapy, analysis, and in mental out-patient departments, etc. Maybe the research is all the more scientific for being of a free-lance variety, and not subject to "planning" and institutionalisation.

Obviously the Committee has not read or understood the enormous quantity of scientific literature on this subject. As regards every doctor endorsing a planned research idea, my rough guess is that if he had more knowledge of psychopathology, he might well suggest that the "planned research" turn its attention to the other side of the picture, namely to the unwarranted and undue morbid anxiety that sexual deviation is likely to lead to degeneration and ruination. Maybe the only terrible thing it is likely to lead to is five or ten years' or life imprisonment. Perhaps if all that nonsense were removed, there would be less anxiety and less homosexuality. After all, this is a phenomenon like every other phenomenon, which nature has produced in the same way as she produces many other curious things.

However the Wolfenden Committee, in spite of its endless incongruities, is not entirely ignorant, perhaps thanks to medical and other witnesses, of the fact that homosexuality is more of a bogy (which the heterosexual, and often the homosexual, man is trying to exterminate), than anything else. It even goes so far as to say that there seems to be no evidence that homosexuality causes the decay of civilisation, or could cause Britain to degenerate or decay.

It seems likely that this has something to do with the Committee's first and only important recommendation, that "homosexual behaviour between consenting adults in private be no longer a criminal offence." They arrive at it through an extraordinary ramble of philosophical and legal thinking, in which a plausible attempt is made to distinguish "sin," a religious concept, from infringement of the "law," a secular matter. Apparently the public has little difficulty in the ordinary course of thinking and behaving in distinguishing between private and group freedom of thought and behaviour (we even go so far as to allow primitive tribes to retain their religious beliefs and customs), and the infringement of some of the liberty of some non-consenting person, whether in the form of assault or otherwise. But in this matter of homosexuality, it would seem that the horror of the concept or phantasy is so great that a tremendous fuss has to be made and endless arguments have to be adduced to suggest that the public should not themselves here be the aggressors and interferers, however satisfied all the other parties concerned may be not to be interfered with. Apparently society and the law do not feel the same compulsive need to interfere in any other form of behaviour, including heterosexuality—though there was a time when they did.

Preceding the famous recommendation, there is a characteristic preamble, of which I shall quote a small portion, although I have mentioned it previously:

> Unless a deliberate attempt is to be made by society, acting through the agency of the law, *to equate the sphere of crime with that of sin, there must remain a realm of private morality and immorality which is, in brief and crude terms, not the law's business.* (My italics.)

And wiser still:

> . . . to emphasise the personal and private nature of moral or immoral conduct is to emphasise the personal and private responsibility which a mature agent can properly be expected to carry for himself without the threat of punishment from the law.

So far, so good, but I think we should not be distracted by one or two good points in the recommendations into forgetting the relatively enormous lost opportunities, and indeed the complete blindness to the opportunity of exposing the inadequacy of punishment as a treatment. Admittedly the public have to be protected from such persons who would interfere unnecessarily with the liberty of its members, but by the same token the homosexuals, like those who prefer cinemas on Sundays, should be protected from the unnecessary interference of the public.

In his recent book *Why I am not a Christian*, Bertrand Russell says: "Perhaps it is the essence of a wise social system to label a number of harmless actions 'Sin,' but tolerate those who perform them. In this way the pleasure of wickedness can be obtained without harm to anyone!" He goes on to say: "The conception of Sin which is bound up with Christian ethics is one that does an extraordinary amount of harm, since it affords people an outlet for their sadism which they believe to be legitimate, and even noble."

It is astonishing, in view of some of the material collected by the Wolfenden Committee, however superficial (for instance the Police Court cases, paragraphs 112, 129 *et seq.*) that the conclusions and recommendations should be so inadequate and in most cases so unsympathetic, or even savage.

I think this can only be explained on the basis of the phenomenon familiar to analysts, namely that while many of the deliberations have in them some feeling and sympathetic understanding, this is interspersed with, particularly when it comes to making a recommendation, a regression to emotionally determined thoughts and behaviour, belonging to the familiar level where everything is either good or bad, and there is no penalty too bad for the bad, indeed the gratification, if it can be "justified" or rationalised, of the superego element in our unconscious conflict. A factor in this phenomenon is the familiar one of having conceded a little in favour of the id (probably felt to be the Devil), one has to put a proportionate emphasis on one's hostility to it, even to the degree of *increasing* some already absurdly retributive penalties.

In most social groups, and in a large proportion of commonplace social gatherings, anybody who talked in the tone of the Wolfenden Report would be promptly dubbed a prig or a fool, but it seems a general principle that when we parade ourselves in public, or appear in print, we must pretend to these exclusively superego principles. They are naturally accompanied by a clamping down on all the real sources of knowledge, both within us and without. Pretense and open eyes do not go together and no doubt the Wolfenden Committee missed a great deal, if not all, of very relevant material (for instance, not a single prostitute and few, if any, truly representative homosexuals, appeared to give evidence).

A leading venereologist, who tells me that he treats as many homosexual persons as heterosexual, and who has a very long experience, expressed two opinions which one would have thought sufficiently superficial to appear in the Wolfenden Report. His first was that an important factor in driving men to homosexuality was (a) fear of making a woman pregnant and (b) fear of venereal disease. (Later they learnt to their cost that venereal disease was at least as frequent among homosexuals as heterosexuals.) The other factor which he seemed quite sure was much more important than was generally appreciated was the economic factor. He said: "A lot of these lads are not really homosexual at all. I should say perhaps eighty per cent of them. I don't mean just the homosexual prostitutes. They get into or maintain a homosexual relationship with a sugar-daddy just because it relieves them of their economic struggle. The genuine homosexual, of which there are relatively few, commonly shows a great lust which these others do not show." (It should be mentioned that this subject of economics as a great "danger" is touched upon in paragraph 97 of the Report.)

Certain points of similarity with normal heterosexual life appear to one in this connection, namely for instance that many women do not partake of sex because of genuine heterosexual desire but because it fits better into the economic system, and this naturally applies to marriage even more than to prostitution. A doctor probably sees more husbands complaining that their wives are frigid than wives complaining that their husbands are impotent (which usually means repressed homosexuality).

For instance, one would hardly expect anything scientific

or reasonable to emerge from deliberations which are, like many legal rulings in other fields, based on arbitrary premises determined by emotions, and therefore we get these absurd difficulties in practically every paragraph, if not in every line of the Report. For instance, (paragraph 70), they admit, "to fix the age (of consent) at twenty-one (or indeed at any age above seventeen) raises particular difficulties in this connection, for it involves leaving liable to prosecution a young man of almost twenty-one for actions which in a few days' time he could perform without breaking the law"—a ridiculous enough position. The Report remarks that the age of consent in heterosexual intercourse is sixteen, so it would seem that the male needs more protection than the female, and there are innumerable other little incongruities which result from these unscientific and arbitrary decisions, all tending to prove that between the interstices of reason, the repressed conflict works its way through to give vent to the sadism of the superego.

But the Report has the courage blatantly to say that though the maximum penalty for seduction of an immature female (i.e., under the age of sixteen) is no more than two years' imprisonment, the equivalent act with a boy under the age of sixteen is *imprisonment for life*. This is the maximum penalty as it stands at present, but the Wolfenden Committee recommends that it should not be altered. Its only revision of maximum penalties is in the direction of increasing them where possible. There is one apparent exception to this rule, but on examination it proves to be only apparent. It is that buggery be reclassified as a misdemeanour instead of a felony. This, as the Report points out, means only that classifying it as a felony would incriminate the doctor who is told about it, and of course homosexuals should be encouraged to confess and doctors to listen to them.

In short, it is a reclassification designed to protect the doctor-patient relationship.

Lest some may feel that I have not substantiated my case of alleged incongruity both in deliberations and in recommendations in the Wolfenden Report, I will quote a sample of utterances that it is difficult to correlate rationally, though it is easy to see the unconscious mental mechanisms at work. As has been mentioned, resulting from the enlightenment gained from medical and other witnesses, the Committee concluded there was no evidence that homosexuality causes the decay of civilisation, or could cause Britain to degenerate or decay. It says (paragraph 98):

> It is a view widely held, and one which found favour among our police and legal witnesses, that seduction in youth is the decisive factor in the production of homosexuality as a condition, and we are aware that this view has done much to alarm parents and teachers. We have found no convincing evidence in support of this contention. Our medical witnesses unanimously hold that seduction has little effect in inducing a settled pattern of homosexual behaviour, and we have been given no grounds from other sources which contradict their judgment. Moreover, it has been suggested to us that the fact of being seduced often does less harm to the victim than the publicity which attends the criminal proceedings against the offender and the distress which undue alarm sometimes leads parents to show.
>
> We have, it is true, found that men charged with homosexual offences frequently plead that they were seduced in their youth, but we think that this plea is a rationalisation or an excuse, and that the offender was predisposed to homosexual behaviour before the "seduction" took place.

Now listen to the *penalties* which the Committee recommends *and the reasons which it gives for them:* (1) Life imprisonment for a grave offence with a boy under sixteen (as now); (2) ten years for indecent assault (against the will of the partner, or with those under sixteen); (3) five years for a grave offence or gross indecency by an over-twenty-one with a youngster between sixteen and twenty-one; and (4) two years for a grave offence or gross indecency by a man under twenty-one with a consenting partner over sixteen, or in public.

These penalties are mostly increased to protect the young. With regard to their severity compared with penalties for equivalent behaviour against the opposite sex, the Report says: "We are inclined to agree, but we feel that any step which might be interpreted as minimising the seriousness of assaults on young persons is to be deprecated." The incongruity of the recently formed opinion of the Committee, namely that homosexuality will not cause Britain to decay, together with the conclusions derived from medical evidence that seduction in youth is not the main cause of a person becoming homosexual, as against their almost lifelong emotional reactions as expressed in their other pronouncements, that any step which might be interpreted as minimising the seriousness of assaults on young persons—obviously because this is what makes them homosexual and ruins them—brings out in a highlight the extraordinary muddle through which these unanalysed persons had to work.

In other words they are saying on an intellectual or conscious level that they have found no evidence for the popular and police view that seduction in youth produces homosexuality, but in their unconscious they still *feel* (as they felt in adolescence that masturbation would lead to paralysis) that it does, therefore it *must* be exterminated—apparently by the most barbarous penalties, the equivalents of the sadism of the primitive superego.

Many superficial aspects of homosexuality, of homosexual behaviour, of homosexual crime, and of crimes related to homosexuality, are discussed in this Report. As in every field of human life and behaviour, it would seem that every form of expression of conflict has some place. There is a somewhat inadequate reference to blackmail, and the fact that private homosexual activities, being crimes, place the participants in the hands of those particular homosexuals, or pseudo-homosexuals, who are out to extort money from easy victims.

The natural homosexual does not commonly associate his behaviour with anything wicked, sinful or criminal. Therefore it comes to him as a terrible shock when he finds that his partner is using the law for the diabolical purpose of extorting money under the most terrible threats imaginable. From some police cases on record it would seem on the other hand that the law, or the police, are inclined to regard the sexual activity as more horrible or reprehensible than the blackmail, and cases are on record where a man, complaining of this form of blackmail, found to his surprise that he was charged by the police with homosexual crime. Such a case is recorded under paragraph 112, case I, where after seven years' sexual relationship, one of the partners commenced to demand money. When the victim finally complained to the police, the Director of Public Prosecutions advised that both men should be charged with buggery. After pleading guilty they were each sentenced to nine months' imprisonment. Neither man had any previous convictions. Their activities had been entirely private.

It is recorded that of seventy-one cases of blackmail reported to the police in England and Wales in the years 1950 to 1953 inclusive, thirty-two were connected with homosexual activities, but of course everybody knows that a great deal of blackmail, particularly in this field, goes on which never comes to the notice of the police.

Importuning by male persons seems to be the only misdemeanour liable to imprisonment for more than three months where the person charged cannot claim to be tried by a jury. Thus any man is subject to having his life ruined by police evidence alone, without trial by jury. The Committee recommends that this should be amended in paragraph 123 and on page 115, number (xii).

Legal and police attitudes towards homosexuality are full of incongruities, many of which are pointed out in the Wolfenden Report. For instance, some local authorities make by-laws regarding the conduct of persons entering or using their public lavatories. These by-laws frequently provide penalties for indecent behaviour, and these apply to homosexual behaviour, in which case under the by-law the penalty may not exceed a fine of five pounds. Of course, if the accused is unfortunate enough to be prosecuted other than under the by-law, there is no knowing what crushing penalty he may receive. It is recognised that these public lavatories are a happy-hunting-ground for many homosexuals, despite the obvious dangers involved. There is perhaps something in homosexuality more than in heterosexuality of an immature phantasy nature, which must be kept removed from any reality exposure or analysis in order to preserve its excitement and pleasure. It is, as it were, something thrilling—(sex) in the dark. In this connection it was put forward that there would be less public lavatory nuisance if the lavatories were better lit, but statistics showed that just as many offences occurred in very well-lit lavatories as in very dark ones.

Homosexuals who loiter in lavatories can of course be any degree of nuisance according to the psychology of their victim, but I think it would always be found that if the "victim" takes no notice of them whatsoever, they make no advances. It would appear that this is a particular form of perversion, not only in the active party, but also in the passive. One has even heard of people of great eminence who have flirted with this form of behaviour. One such gentleman, a bachelor, after a long and blameless life, just after he had retired, apparently instituted his own neurotic penalty (incidentally almost as sadistic as those instituted by the law). He got a severe left-sided torticollis (wry-neck), which nothing would put right. In consequence he had to walk with his head looking over his left shoulder, and practically feeling his way about. He would not have believed that sex had anything to do with it. Of course in a sense it had not, this was not sex, this was the opposite: punishment.

His history revealed that from an early age his only sexual pleasure had been that of standing in certain lavatories in the hope of feeling the man standing beside him, or being felt by him. He knew this was terribly dangerous, and for some reason he usually turned to the right when he entered a urinal, so that the entrance was on his left-hand side. During the moment of acute sexual excitement he would be watching over his left shoulder to see if anybody—in particular the lavatory attendant was coming in. Thus the conflict between his pleasure phantasies and desires on the one hand, and his anxiety on the other, were joined. He was never caught, but when he reached the age of fifty-five, suddenly, it seems, guilt and anxiety won the day; he completely stopped all these debasing activities, went over to the other side of the conflict, was inclined to deny the whole story of his life, and to pretend that he had never felt any sexuality at all. But at the same time this extreme and painful torticollis descended upon him.

I telephoned the doctor who had sent him to me, and said: "At fifty-five this may be a very long case, particularly as he is so full of resistances. Could you perhaps try some of your methods first? For instance, if you got him a masseur to massage his neck, and if some sublimated homosexual rapport developed between them, do you think that might be a quicker way of helping this poor man?"

The doctor, who was very *au fait* in these matters replied, laughing: "Good heavens, doctor, I thought you would know better than that. Don't you know that it isn't the slightest bit of use unless it happens in a lavatory?"

Obviously there is a lot of psychology and psychopathology to be revealed in such cases, as there is in the case of men who prefer a succession of prostitutes, and of women, including prostitutes, who prefer a succession of unknown men. But if this psychopathology is unravelled, it may be found that it is merely divergent and is quite strongly interwoven with what is called normal sex or love and hate relationships.

From most of the cases that come to see a doctor or psychiatrist, it is clear that a great deal of conflict between their more or less compulsive desire, comparable to the heterosexual desire, on the one hand, and attempts to control or repress it on the other, have taken place. Of course this is obvious in such cases as the one just described, where it was finally revealed that his castrating superego won the life battle. Now this intrapsychic conflict goes through the mechanisms of most conflicts in the unconscious; that is to say it tends to be projected into the world of reality around it. Put rather too briefly one may say instead of eradicating the source of guilt feelings *inside us*, if we can find these "wicked" tendencies in some *other* person, particularly if he has given himself away, we then have a scapegoat ready to hand. It is so much more comfortable to exterminate, put in prison for life, punish, and all that sort of thing, *somebody else*, than to suffer internally ourselves. At last we know where the sin lies—in *that* fellow—and we can "let him have it." Thereby we escape, or we gratify at least one side or one part of our intra-psychic conflict.

It is through such unconscious processes as these that there spring up such extraordinary phenomena as the witch trials and the Inquisition. Sexuality has always been very near the witch or demon, and this is much easier to rationalise if it is homosexuality. But to maintain such attitudes as these without insight, and thereby, of course, to avoid the neurosis or prison ourselves, we have to create in our own minds this peculiar bias which prevents us from understanding. To my mind it can be regarded as a mass psychosis, as will be pointed out in great detail in a forthcoming publication of mine.

Finally, the Wolfenden Report gets on to what it is pleased to call "the treatment of offenders." We cannot blame exclusively the members of the Committee for the extraordinary muddle to which these deliberations lead, for the public in general, including the jurists and educated public, have never sorted out in their minds, or successfully examined, the scientific principles involved in crime and punishment, and in what they presume to call "treatment." Even when the process is frankly called "punishment," emotionally charged factors in the punisher are practically the only determinants that one can discover. There is some recognition of this in the Wolfenden deliberations, when they say, regarding the "lack of uniformity in the treatment of offenders by the courts" (para. 177):

> While we are therefore not able to suggest any positive remedy, we call attention to the matter and to the desirability of the courts' dealing dispassionately with every homsexual offence, giving proper weight to the reformative as well as to the deterrent or preventive aspects.

There is no doubt that the strongest emotional force involved, though often disavowed (as in this instance), in punishment is retribution or revenge. If somebody stamps on one's foot, one is apt not to deal "dispassionately" with his offence, or to give proper weight to reformative, deterrent, or preventive aspects. One is more likely to kick him as hard as one can! And that is retribution. It is a natural emotional reaction and may have nothing reasonable behind it. Perhaps the Chinese were more frank about the phenomenon of "punishment" or "treatment." Their ancient book of rites specifies only one punishment—cutting off the head!

While various cultural developments commonly, but not always, preclude such overt and natural reactions, it may be that in our retention of life-imprisonment as a punishment (or "treatment"), for instance for buggery with a boy under the age of sixteen, we are approximating as near as we dare to the natural, overwhelming emotion of retribution. Thus we see that the Wolfenden Committee, in considering "the law and practice relating to homosexual offences and the treatment of persons convicted of such offences by the courts" (paragraph 1 [a]), is working on a special branch of a subject, the general principles of which have not been clarified, and are thus already muddled up by unclear premises.

It may here be mentioned that it is obvious to the therapist, who has to wean people from neurosis, delinquency or psychosis, that the display of any form of hostility—and punishment certainly displays hostility—brings all therapeutic measures to an end. I am now more inclined to the opinion that fear, such as the fear of punishment, does or can have some deterrent effect, but not nearly so great as is popularly supposed. I once had a patient whom it was very difficult to cure of his mackintosh fetishism, but when he was arrested by the police for looking through the bushes in the rain at girls taking shelter in a women's park lavatory, was so terrified that he suppressed such impulses for at least six months. Fortunately the police could not begin to understand his motives, and so no charge was actually brought against him. Fear thus had a deterrent effect, but it produced an increase in his anxiety neurosis.

The question here may well be, are we trying to win the abnormal person back to normality, or are we trying to protect society from the nuisance this abnormality causes? If merely the latter, then the Chinese were right, the surest way is to cut off his head . . . or send him to life imprisonment. If the former, we will almost certainly fail if we contaminate our treatment with anything such as punishment, which reveals hostility. The man already has an intra-psychic conflict and in getting us to punish him he is merely coercing us into taking sides with one side of that conflict, maybe so that he can subsequently enjoy greater freedom with the other side. The therapist's job may indeed be to save him from a too-dramatic acting out of his conflict, such as suicide.

The difficulty that has to be faced by the community is the conflict between nuisance or injury to the public and the well-being of the individual, through whom alone can therapeutic success be gained. No doubt most of us would say that the matter of first importance is to protect the public; hence we have the legal institutions of capital punishment and life imprisonment. But do not let us get confused between this public-protection motive and therapy. The trouble is that not only do we get confused, but each motive is apt to exceed its assignment, so that we begin poking our noses in where the public has no business, and making criminals where none exists.

It is interesting to note that although the maximum punishments, particularly in regard to homosexual offences, seem to be so savagely out of proportion to the damage caused, nevertheless in the courts themselves it is more usual (though not usual enough) to find "justice," with the maximum punishment principle tempered with mercy—if anything can be merciful after the public exposure of an individual's sexual practices. The Wolfenden Report tells us that though imprisonment is "the punishment prescribed by law for homosexual offences . . . only a minority of homosexual offenders are sent to prison. For instance, in 1955 only thirty per cent . . . and in Scotland, during the same year, only thirty-seven per cent." (Paragraph 149.) It is noteworthy that this is not a very small percentage. Other "treatments" and punishments included absolute discharge, conditional discharge, binding over, probation, and fine. It is noteworthy that "thirty per cent of the persons convicted in 1955 of homosexual offences punishable with imprisonment were fined instead." (Paragraph 158.)

In the case of young offenders the equivalent punishments

are Borstal training,* detention in a detention center, committal to an Approved School, committal to the care of a fit person, and attendance at an Attendance Center. The last three are for offenders under seventeen years of age.

It seems to me possible that the discrepancy between the theoretically laid-down (maximum) penalties for homosexual behaviour and some of these relatively "minor" executions is due to the fact that the court has had the opportunity of making the acquaintance of the accused, thereby discovering that he is not so terrible as the abstract conception paints him. One may add that were it possible for the punishers to mix freely in the lives of the alleged culprits, and really get to know them, their outlook, and even their way of life and delinquent behaviour, the compulsion to punish might increasingly give way to understanding and therapy, at least in a large number of cases. As Barbara Wootton put it: "The concept of illness expands continually at the expense of the concept of moral failure."

In passing it should be mentioned that the Wolfenden Committee rejected the proposition that homosexuality should be regarded as a "disease." They naïvely remark that "to decide the most appropriate method of treatment of a particular offender is a much more difficult problem for the courts than the decision as to his guilt." (Paragraph 169.) I say "naïvely" because I can think of no person or body of persons less well qualified to assess an "appropriate method of treatment" than those associated with the courts.

A similar statement is (paragraph 170): "Apart altogether

---

* A method of treatment of juvenile delinquents up to twenty-one years of age by the Borstal Association, established by act of Parliament in 1908. It stresses good living conditions and physical and vocational training.

from any considerations of retribution the objectives of penal sanctions are deterrence, prevention and reformation." The truth is that the act of punishment is determined by the reaction of retribution, which is powerful enough to brush all else aside. This "criminal" act is then rationalised, and even sanctified, by the high ideals of "deterrence," "prevention" and "reformation."

It reminds me of a patient I once had, whose father (a jurist) used periodically to order him to come to his study for punishment. He would be ordered to bend over the bed while the father delicately and lovingly removed his shorts and any underwear, and went on to stroke his behind before proceeding to the inevitable caning. To my mind there was little doubt that the father, like the son, was a repressed homosexual. But the point I wish to bring out here is that the father invariably sanctified his act by saying to the boy, "You must always remember that this is for your own good." (Deterrence, prevention and reformation.) I can remember also the son's description of his reaction! It was only fear that kept him from murder. Is this the "treatment" which the law institutes?

If we bear in mind the very small percentage of homosexual crimes which are detected by the law—one in thirty thousand —we may find it easy to believe that the deterrent which outweighs all others is the fear of detection. Perhaps it outweighs all others in the proportion of one to thirty thousand. In this case we may say that it really does not matter what these sanctions and punishments amount to, execution or one's photograph in the local newspaper, they are all completely dwarfed by the danger of exposure and perhaps by the disgrace, etc., following such exposure. Thus the one concern of the delinquent, be it in the homosexual sphere or in any other, is that he shall not be discovered, particularly by the police. This brings one to the view that if discovery were always inevitable, be it in the sphere of homosexuality or in any other sphere of crime, then crime simply would not take place. Our conclusion may be that deliberation as to what you do with the mouse when you catch it is entirely irrelevant, because the first thing is to catch it. Are we just exercising a little game to express some of our unconscious tendencies and enhance our phantasy of omnipotence? Perhaps it would be better to have a committee on how to apprehend crime or the criminal before we proceed to a discussion as to what to do with him. Otherwise he is, in nearly thirty thousand cases to one, prescribing and carrying out his own "treatment."

Another point the Wolfenden Committee brings out and debunks is the popular illusion that treatment is something which can take place in prison. I shall not go into details but they rightly come to the decision that it cannot. In any case, prison and treatment are incompatible.

No doubt there is something to be learned from the Wolfenden Report, particularly if, like most of the members, we knew nothing about homosexuality to start with. For instance, it is brought out that the ordinary adult homosexual, who has integrated his sexual life with that of friendship, love or passion towards another adult male, is often just as shocked by the male who pursues lads of fifteen or under, as the average heterosexual man would be at a man who pursued young girls or children for sexual purposes. In short, to the "normal" person, heterosexual or homosexual, *paedicatio* is as reprehensible as *paedicatio mulierum*. The natural male homosexual resents very strongly any confusion of his proclivities or those of his friends with the abnormal "perverted" proclivities of such a deviant.

The latter are possibly more frequently apprehended and would therefore, in police courts and prisons, suggest a higher proportion of homosexuals than is truly representative. "Of 1,022 men in prison for homosexual offences in 1954, no fewer than 590 (58%) were involved in offences against boys aged fifteen or under." It is noteworthy also that "236 of these had previous convictions for homosexual offences. Further, of the 1,022 prisoners, 211 (21.6%) had four or more previous convictions of one kind of another recorded against them and of these 102 (10%) had seven or more . . . the Cambridge survey indicates that two-thirds of the sexual recidivists under review had previous convictions for sexual offences only, and that generally there was a similarity between the repeated offences." (Paragraph 202.)

This last remark reminds the therapist that practically all patients who come to him for treatment, not only homosexuals but all those suffering from neurosis, and especially from minor psychosis, are incredibly resistant to giving up one iota of their beliefs, delusions, or reactive patterns. A patient once said to me: "But doctor, if you take that murder impulse away from me, it will no longer be *me*. I shall have nothing to live for. I would feel already dead." This may give us a slight conception of the resistance to even minor modifications, let alone "cure." (Perhaps the Chinese were right!)

I do not know much about resistance to medical or surgical interference for therapeutic purposes, but as regards estrogen (paragraph 209) a doctor who tried it on a transvestite patient whom I sent him, told me that the man refused to go on with the treatment *because it made him so miserable*. No doubt the surgical treatment of castration would tend similarly to make the victim miserable, though there are some countries where it

is practised with the consent of the offender. The Wolfenden
Committee rejected it on the grounds that the operation removes neither the desires nor the ability to fulfil them, for instance in the case of a passive male homosexual.

The two doctors on the Committee (Curran and Whitby)
emphasise some interesting points. For instance, they rightly
say that "the same criminal act may be committed as a piece of
adolescent experimentation; or it may be the result of temporary or permanent mental or physical disorder or disease; or it
may be part of the individual's life style." In short, "that there
is a great variety of problems, that the significance of offences
varies with the individual offender . . . that individual cases
may require individual treatment, does not always lead to their
application in practice . . . The large group of youngsters
and young men with what is often called 'transitional' homosexuality is especially important." (Pages 72, 73 *et seq.*)

They quote Dr. T. C. N. Gibbens (in a paper entitled "The
Sexual Behaviour of Young Criminals") as saying, after studying two hundred Borstal lads: "Perhaps the most important
point that has to be made about homosexuality is that it should
not be considered in isolation from heterosexuality. The issues
are those of sexuality, with homosexual and heterosexual com-
ponents in each case."

Drs. Curran and Whitby emphasise also that many males
pass through a homosexual phase satisfactorily and without
medical help. It makes one reflect that it is rather unfortunate
if any of these are apprehended during this transient phase, and
thereby perhaps prevented from leading a normal sexual life.

The doctors think a high proportion of homosexual cases
have associated psychiatric abnormality. They agree with the
recommendation that, with the patient's consent, estrogen

treatment should be permitted in suitable cases in prison. They recommend also a more extended resort to probation with a condition of medical treatment, as mentioned in paragraph 200, although evidence is that the treatment under these auspices is unsuccessful.

Although the Committee generally agrees that the duration of a prison sentence should not be decided on purely therapeutic grounds (page 76), it is added that "our medical witnesses were unanimous that cases did occur in which a prison sentence could have therapeutic value." I am perfectly certain that this is a fond delusion. The only "therapeutic value" there can possibly be is that of the patient either being frightened and thereby deterred in his overt freedom, or/and his deceiving the doctors and perhaps even himself for the sake of "peace of mind." After all, you *must* go over to the side of the people who can apprehend and imprison you like this, even if it gives you a state of internal tension or nervous breakdown.

There are perhaps a few other "discoveries" which should be tabulated. The Committee agrees that most homosexual behaviour is due to the existence of the "homosexual propensity" in a greater or lesser degree in one or both of the participants. However, they conclude that they have no idea what this homosexual propensity is. If this is the basis of the whole trouble, perhaps they should have ceased work on that note.

Their remark that they have encountered several cases in which men have got into touch with homosexual offenders whose convictions were reported in the press (paragraph 218), with the result that further homosexual offences were committed, reminds one of the report that when in the good old days pickpockets were being hanged at Tyburn, it was said that all the pickpockets in London were active amongst the spectators. So much for the deterrent effect of punishment. Obviously the only deterrent would be the certainty or likelihood of apprehension.

"To ensure that men guilty of homosexual offences are not allowed to continue in the teaching profession" (para. 219) is of course only common sense, and no doubt relevant to the principle of prevention, provided a distinction is made between the ordinary "mature" male homosexual, who consorts with adults, and the paederast. Another common sense preventive measure, or at least precautionary measure, is the by-law prevalent in some places in Scotland, making it an offence to stay unduly long in a public lavatory. (Para. 220)

After over three years of deliberations, the members of the Wolfenden Committee arrived at the following recommendations, regarding the law and practice relating to homosexual offences, and the treatment of persons convicted of such offences by the courts. Although we have singled out the only important or revolutionary one of these, and lightly dismissed most of the others as trivial, it may be desired by those who have not had access to the Wolfenden Report to know exactly what these were. The Committee tabulated them as follows:

1. That homosexual behaviour between consenting adults in private be no longer a criminal offence (paragraph 62).
2. That questions relating to "consent" and "in private" be decided by the same criteria as apply in the case of heterosexual acts between adults (paragraphs 63, 64).
3. That the age of "adulthood" for the purposes of the proposed change in the law be fixed at twenty-one (paragraph 71).
   (As mentioned, there was a lot of discussion about this as

the age of consent in heterosexual intercourse is sixteen, but finally twenty-one was decided upon.)

4. That no proceedings be taken in respect of any homosexual act (other than an indecent assault) committed in private by a person under twenty-one, except by the Directors of Public Prosecutions or with the sanction of the Attorney-General (paragraph 72).

5. That the law relating to living on the earnings of prostitution be applied to the earnings of male, as well as female, prostitution (paragraph 76).

   (It is doubtful whether any person, female or male, is really in the position of "slave-labour" imagined by some members of the public.)

6. That the law be amended, if necessary, so as to make it explicit that the term "brothel" includes premises used for homosexual practices (paragraph 76).

7. That there be introduced revised maximum penalties in respect of buggery, gross indecency and indecent assaults (paragraphs 90, 91).

8. That buggery be re-classified as a misdemeanour (paragraph 94). (As mentioned this was not to diminish the offence; on the contrary, the penalties for buggery exceed those of any other form of homosexual act, starting with life imprisonment if with a boy under the age of sixteen, and five years' imprisonment for a boy above the age of sixteen, below the age of twenty-one [in circumstances not amounting to indecent assault—which carries ten years]. This five-year imprisonment penalty is an increase recommended by the Committee on the present law. It seems incongruous, as there is no penalty whatsoever for

the equivalent heterosexual act with a consenting female of this age.)

9. That except for some grave reason, proceedings be not instituted in respect of homosexual offences incidentally revealed in the course of investigating allegations of blackmail (paragraph 112).

10. That Section 29 (3) of the Larceny Act, 1916, be extended so as to apply to all homosexual offences (paragraph 113).

11. That the offence of gross indecency between male persons be made triable summarily with the consent of the accused (paragraph 114).

12. That male persons charged with importuning for immoral purposes be entitled to claim trial by jury (paragraph 123).

13. That except for indecent assaults, the prosecution of any homosexual offence more than twelve months old be barred by statute (paragraph 135).

14. That subject to any necessary special safeguards, managers and headmasters of approved schools be allowed the same measure of discretion in dealing with homosexual behaviour between inmates as that enjoyed by those responsible for the management of any other educational establishment (paragraph 147).

15. That the organisation, establishment and conditions of service of the prison medical service be reviewed (paragraph 180).

16. That a court by which a person under twenty-one is found guilty of a homosexual offence be required to obtain and consider a psychiatric report before passing sentence (paragraph 187).

17. That prisoners desirous of having estrogen treatment be

permitted to do so if the prison medical officer considers that this would be beneficial (paragraph 211).

18. That research be instituted into the aetiology of homo-sexuality and the effects of various forms of treatment (paragraph 216).

The remaining thirteen members of the Committee, two, as mentioned, having resigned about eighteen months previously, signed these recommendations, six with reservations. As has been mentioned, Mr. Adair's reservation was a disagreement with the principal recommendation—number one—eloquently urged. The distinction between buggery and other homo-sexual offences was objected to by four members, including two women and the two doctors. Dr. Whitby has some further reservations, chiefly aimed at making no distinction between buggery and indecent assault (carrying a maximum penalty of ten years' imprisonment), and in minor cases between buggery with consent and gross indecency (penalty two years imprison-ment). At the same time he stresses that the effects of homosex-ual seduction in youth have been greatly exaggerated. He says: "Whatever moral damage may be done, the effect of seduction over . . . the age of sixteen . . . is unlikely to be that of pro-ducing a homosexual deviation in one who is predominantly heterosexual." (Page 125.)

Dr. Curran in his "further reservation" carries these ob-jections a good deal further. He would like to "make the maxi-mum sentence for indecent assault two years instead of ten years." He emphasises that "the law itself probably makes little difference to the amount of homosexual behaviour which ac-tually occurs; whatever the law may be, there will always be strong social forces opposed to homosexual behaviour. These strong social forces are, I believe, specially operative in the case of paedophiliacs, whose conduct is universally reprobated, not least by other homosexuals. Paedophiliacs act in isolation from the homosexuals, and are not accepted in homosexual coteries or groups." (Page 126.)

In keeping with my views, Dr. Curran goes on to say: "I understand it has long been common ground in the opinion of those best qualified to judge that it is not the severity of the punishment that is most important for deterrence; it is the certainty—or high degree of probability—that punishment will actually result. If correct, this principle has special application to all homosexual crimes owing to the vast discrepancy between the number of criminal acts and the conviction rate . . . Can it seriously be supposed that those who are guilty of indecent assault work out 'betting odds' of this kind (the number of years in prison) before they indulge in their acts? And if they did, what deterrent effect would it be likely to have?"

And further: "It seems to me that the sole, and very proper, justification for long sentences is to keep out of harm's way those who have repeatedly shown themselves to be public menaces and concerning whom nothing else, in the present state of knowledge, can be done."

But it seems the length of the prison sentence is not motivated by such considerations, as Dr. Curran points out in his following paragraphs, where he shows that thirty-two of fifty-four men sentenced to prison had no previous convictions, and no other offences were taken into consideration. He suggests that the severity of the punishments reveals principally retribution. I agree.

When Dr. Curran suggests that in the present state of our knowledge nothing else can be done, I would like to add that what could be done is an alteration in our attitude. We protect the public from dangerous lunatics and mental defectives without bringing into the picture ideas of crime and punishment— or retribution. The attitude of mind is different, and much might be learned from it.

Regarding importuning, Dr. Curran says: "I can see no logical reason why male importuning should be treated differently from female solicitation." His further remarks are of interest: "Males seldom importune other males who do not give them encouragement. Their activities are less obvious, and more subtle and discreet, than is the case with female solicitation. Consequently, as I believe, the general public greatly underestimate (as do the criminal statistics) the amount of male importuning that goes on. Further, the number of male importuners who are prostitutes is admittedly extremely small; very few male importuners are out for financial gain." He does not consider that a relaxation of the penalties on male importuning would result in an increase or a public nuisance, as other members of the Committee appeared to think. He considers that the same safeguards and penalties as are proposed for common prostitutes would provide an adequate safeguard against the development of brazen activities on the part of male importuners which might be publicly offensive.

Doctors and psychiatrists, and of course particularly analysts, learn so much of the private sexual life of their patients, that they cannot always maintain the horrified attitude of the layman and pretend that sexuality, even homosexuality, is something exceptional, perhaps something to be denied and certainly execrated. They have come nearer to recognising that knowledge as the only answer to all the problems here presented. Nevertheless it would seem that even doctors and psychiatrists, presented with the atmosphere of the law-courts, and I think that the Wolfenden Committee presented much of such an atmosphere, are not immune, unconsciously at least, to the influence which this atmosphere has upon our ever-wobbling conflicts, even if they are on a conscious plane, that is to say a more superficial plane and reinforced by knowledge of that which the superego denies.

This seems to me the only explanation as to why doctors, like the two on this Committee, who are accustomed in their consulting rooms to hearing the truth about sexuality, and gaining scientific knowledge of its various manifestations, should move so far towards conciliating the superego representatives by whom they were heavily outnumbered. Perhaps it is only the analyst, who has had his knowledge of the instinct reservoir of the id and the vicissitudes of the libido thoroughly engrained, who can be relied upon to resist the folly of pretence and not be taken in by "respectability." I may add, however, that even the analyst's knowledge is superficial, relevant to his engrained and indoctrinated reactive patterns of his earlier life, and it is not impossible for him too to succumb in very legal atmosphere to feeling that nature is sinful and wicked.

There are other reactive patterns with which we are less familiar, and which therefore may strike us as so very odd when we encounter them in our work. I was consulted by a man whom I shall describe as qualifying, on superficial manifestations, for the late Dr. Kinsey's number four or five hetero-homosexual rating. He was a great big powerful fellow. He alleged that he had enough heterosexuality in him to justify his hope of being cured of his homosexual tendencies. The evidence for this was that he had on several occasions performed the heterosexual act successfully, and had for a time even lived with a woman with some degree of sexual relationship. At one of his early sessions he told me that he had a confession to make; he had been so emotionally worked up by the music of an opera that he had left the opera-house, gone to a nearby railway station and looked for a man. In a few minutes his solicitations were successful; but walking home with the man, he decided that he did not like him, and so said goodbye and went back to the station, where he found another unknown man with whom everything went successfully.

I had already begun to feel that this practising homosexual was a poor bid for analytical success, and therefore, most unanalytically, I taxed him with the question: "You come here allegedly to be cured of your homosexuality, to become heterosexual, and yet even while under treatment, when your sexual feelings are aroused by the music, you leave the opera and look for a *man*. In the circumstances, if you had to look for a sexual partner, why on earth didn't you look for a woman?"

This huge man rolled over on to his side, half sat up and stared me in the face: "Good heavens!" he said, "I had never thought of that. Good heavens! Pick up a woman? Why, I wouldn't have a clue!"

Thus it may be recognised that what to the heterosexual man may present little difficulty, namely that of making the acquaintance of an unknown woman, or easier still perhaps, picking up a prostitute, had no pattern in this homosexual's psyche. It seems to me that one might have asked the average heterosexual man to go to a railway station and "pick up" an unknown *man*. What he probably would pick up would be a plain-clothes detective, with the well-known results! And perhaps the exceptional cases to which fate is so unkind are the less homosexual ones. These libidinal relationships between persons are obviously something which emanates from deeper unconscious emotional or instinctual sources, and cannot be taken over by the ego at anyone's command. All that the ego can do is to sit in judgment over them, and dole out punishment.

Now perhaps I ought to ask myself why it is that in reading this beautifully worded and beautifully reasoned report *my* first emotional reaction is one of indignation and contempt. I think the answer, or one of the answers, may well be this: Throughout one's many years of training analysis (for which daily attendance used to be required) one was encouraged in exposing to consciousness proclivities in oneself similar to those exhibited by these gentlemen and ladies of the Wolfenden Committee. One's object was to analyse these proclivities, to trace them to their source and to see how they were made. Quite early one began to discover that these were an enormous defensive construction designed to defend our socially timid and highly susceptible consciousness from a recognition of the, at that time, intolerable truths that dwelt within our unconscious minds, and the unconscious minds of all other persons. Indeed, that is the very source of everything that goes on in us, positive and negative, expressive, prohibitive and defensive. It is only by virtue of years of this self-examination that one qualifies to become an analyst, to be in a position to understand the perplexities in the minds of others.

And now in this year of grace, one meets a representative body of the educated public, who appear to be not even aware of the need, or possibility of the existence, source or mechanisms of these very phenomena which it has been assigned to examine, to pass judgment upon and to make recommendations! The members of this body proceed to struggle with their assignment, their task, from this position of abysmal ignorance. The analyst can see that, like all their beliefs and behaviours, these deliberations and expressions of theirs are determined by conflict, conflict in which, if the superego does not have supreme command behaviouristically, it can at least pretend to such command and allege its omnipotence. Parent images, now represented by society, would tolerate nothing less.

The Report opens with the announcement, "We were appointed on 24th August, 1954," and having read the Report, I am inclined to remark that they do not mention whether it was A.D. or B.C.! It was certainly before psychology or psychoanalysis had been dreamed of, at any rate by them. One could almost imagine the primal-horde-father arriving on the scene and subjecting all the weaker males to general castration all round. This is not so fantastic as it sounds, for in the primitive life of today, more conspicuously among primitive tribes, but also in the primitive life within civilisation (relics of the past), this is what the older generation is doing to the younger, though it is commonly called a "circumcision" rather than a "castration" rite, and tends to become less physical and more mental as civilisation advances. Patients have described to me how their long years of education at public schools and so forth, and the general indoctrination accompanying it, was felt by them to be a protracted "castration." And so it will come out even in the Wolfenden Report!

Not the least of the dangers of this Report is the fact that it is so plausibly and reasonably written. I am a little tempted here to quote several paragraphs to illustrate what I mean by this smooth reasonableness. It tends to lead the reader away from intellectually less satisfying truths, but perhaps I can illustrate what I mean, though not nearly so satisfactorily, by taking a few random excerpts from a succession of sections and leaving the rest to the reader's imagination.

> *Paragraph 66:* It seems to us that there are four sets of considerations which should govern the decision on this point [the age at which a man is regarded as an adult]. The first is connected with the need to protect young and immature persons; the second is connected with the age at which the pattern of a man's sexual development can be said to be fixed; the third is connected with the meaning of the word "adult" in the sense of "responsible for his own actions"; and the fourth is connected with the consequences which would follow from the fixing of any particular age . . .

> *Paragraph 67:* So far as concerns the first set of considerations, we have made it clear throughout our report that we recognise the need for protecting the young and immature . . . and we find it hard to believe that he needs to be protected from would-be seducers more carefully than a girl does . . . On this view, there would be some ground for making sixteen the age of "adulthood," since sexual intercourse with a willing girl of this age is not unlawful.

> *Paragraph 68:* We have given special attention to the evidence which has been given to us in connection with the second set of considerations—those which relate the notion of "adulthood" to a recognisable age in the fixation of a young man's sexual pattern—for we should not wish to see legalised, etc., etc., etc. . . . Our medical witnesses were unanimously of the view that the main sexual pattern is laid down in the early years of life, and the majority of them held that it was usually fixed, in main outline, by the age of sixteen. Many held that it was fixed much earlier . . .

> *Paragraph 70:* To suggest that the age of adulthood for the purposes we have in mind should be twenty-one leads us to the fourth set of considerations we have mentioned, namely, the consequences which would follow from the decision about any particular age. To fix the age at twenty-one (or indeed at

any age above seventeen) raises particular difficulties in this
connection, for it involves leaving liable to prosecution a
young man of almost twenty-one for actions which in a few
days' time he could perform without breaking the law. This
difficulty would admittedly arise whatever age was decided
upon for it would always be the case that an action would be
illegal a few days below that age and legal above it. But this
difficulty would present itself in a less acute form if the age
were fixed at eighteen, which is the other age most frequently
suggested to us. For whereas it would be difficult to regard a
young man of nearly twenty-one charged with a homosexual
offence as a suitable subject for "care or protection" under the
provisions of the Children and Young Persons Acts, it would
not be entirely inappropriate so to regard a youth under
eighteen. If the age of adulthood for the purposes of our
amendment were fixed at eighteen, and if the "care or protection" provisions were extended to cover young persons up to
that age, there would be a means of dealing with homosexual
behaviour by those under that age without invoking the penal
sanctions of the criminal law. [The age finally decided upon
was twenty-one.]

If one reads page after page of this sort of verbiage, one is
apt to be lulled into a more or less acquiescent state of mind, and
to forget that it is mostly a series of platitudes chosen arbitrarily for the sake of arriving at decisions, worked over and
through and through with so much obsessional examination
and re-examination that we gain the impression that everything
possible has been taken into consideration, no detail has been
left out, nobody could contribute any further item to the discussion, and therefore the conclusions and recommendations
framed so smoothly and with such an illusion of reasonableness must be the ultimate truth.

Perhaps they are the ultimate truth, if the truth is debarred

from entering consciousness—and that is the indoctrination
which protects the average person from realising unwanted
truths about himself and others. Perhaps we have to go round
and round in repetitive obsessional circles of deliberations, but
we must ensure that we do not get anywhere near knowing
what we must not know. That would disturb our equilibrium.
Perhaps we find it less anxiety-provoking to be an animal on
the one hand and pretend to be a god on the other. We hope
to convince everybody to our own advantage and we may even
convince ourselves, and how satisfactory it all is!

On the other hand, scientific—especially psychoanalytic—
investigation of the phenomenon of homosexuality is not concerned with these plausible coverings-up and attendant self-
satisfactions. It is concerned with finding out the causes and
psychopathology of the condition, in spite of the resistances in
the mind to allowing these to enter consciousness. Therefore,
like all science, its theories have progressed through a succession
of stages. Originally homosexuality was connected specifically
with aberrations of the Oedipus complex, and there is no doubt
that this is true so far as it goes. We see the patient whose clinical material reveals that he has identified himself with his mother
in an attempt to escape the awful consequences of father-ri-
valry, and so on.

But in recent years some of the very modern analysts claim
to have traced the etiology of homosexuality right back to a
pre-Oedipus level. In doing so they already had a guide from
Freud, for in 1910, writing of Leonardo da Vinci, he said: "We
will for the moment leave aside the question as to what connection there is between homosexuality and sucking at the mother's
breast." Many homosexuals show on the auto-erotic plane oral

fixation and on the object-relationship plane, mother or breast-nipple fixation.

Many years later Freud declared that "the child discovers the pleasure-giving genital zone—penis or clitoris—during sucking. I shall leave it undecided whether the child really takes this newly-acquired source of pleasure as a substitute for the recently lost nipple of the mother's breast."

It has been pointed out that even the homosexual, in common with everybody, had a first and therefore most important experience in life at his mother's breast, or with his mother. Such a first experience must be incorporated into his homosexual phantasies and feelings and activities. It would seem that he has abandoned his mother's breast or nipple by displacement of the effects associated with it, on to the male organs. There is little doubt that this transfer or displacement is attained via the individual's own body, via his own penis, and this has everything to do with the familiar narcissism of the homosexual. He has the whole thing with him, in his person, all the valuable objects, including the first one, his mother's breast or nipple.

One of my homosexual patients, a highly educated and cultured man, who, by the way, did not practise homosexuality, in the course of his analysis related the following very apposite story: He was his mother's darling and as an infant had never been separated from her. Then on his fifth birthday he got scarlet fever. In those days it was compulsory that scarlet fever cases be removed to the fever hospital, and so it came about that that night he found himself disconsolate in a hospital bed, without his mother. He was heartbroken and felt he would die of misery. Then, having nothing to do, he started moving his hands about his body. (I expect he was unconsciously searching for his mother's nipple.) Low down on his abdomen he suddenly came across a spot the sensations from which electrified him. He had found his glans penis. He masturbated for the first time in his life and felt that all was well, and he hardly needed mother any more.

It would seem possible that the homosexual who has orally regressed to the nipple level, perhaps out of some disappointment or imagined let-down by the mother, has unconsciously substituted penis excitement (originally in himself) for the first and greatest pleasure in life at the mother's breast. For a time this valuable source of satisfaction remains with him and is responsible for the well-known "penis-pride" of the boy, but subsequently displacement takes place on to other objects who, like himself, are endowed with this stimulating anatomical structure. Of course other readjustments of the psychic economy takes place, including a repudiation of everything feminine and an increasing canalisation of all sexual potentialities on to this "new"-found form of enjoying the old, repressed and forgotten situation.

After this brief itemised excursion into the realms of psychopathology, can we force ourselves to come back to the Wolfenden Report, with its recommendations based upon newly acquired, superficial "knowledge" of the manisfestations of homosexuality? Unfortunately people who are not fortified with a background of deep psychopathological knowledge, are apt to forget this and transgress into remarks and recommendations which only ignorance would make possible. For instance, in paragraph 200 the Report says: "A prison sentence can, in many cases, detrimentally affect any prospect of successful treatment, so that the offender remains in a state of mind predisposed to the repetition of his offence."

If the members of the Committee really recognise this truth, surely it is incongruous of them in the face of it to support and even to increase penalties of long terms of imprisonment. One may wonder how many conflicting motives are at work in their discussions and recommendations. They go on to say:

> If, by the use of other methods, the offender can be successfully brought to a state of better adjustment to society in which he is less disposed to repeat his offence, then clearly society gains. The Cambridge survey, however, shows that the proportion of homosexual offenders subsequently reconvicted was almost the same in the case of offenders who had been placed on probation (29.9 per cent) as it was in the case of offenders who had been sent to prison (30.1 per cent).

I am glad they make this last confession, because in their deliberations they more or less give the impression that they are the non-sinners holding out a hand to the sinners, and actually use such words as rehabilitation, better integration with social life, higher ideals, a greater degree of sublimation, and so forth. I wondered how they would put this across to such people as Leonardo da Vinci, Julius Ceasar, and in modern times the vast number of eminent men whose names, of course, cannot be mentioned. Naturally the homosexual is not necessarily endowed with greater insight into the psychopathology of homosexuality or of heterosexuality than is the average person, but in the light of what we know of psychology, this does not warrant the heterosexual feeling superior to the homosexual, or regarding him as somebody to whom he can teach better ways.

It occurred to me in reading certain conclusions of the Report, that like the Wolfenden Committee, we are all (or most of us) in one camp, and therefore apt to feel how reasonable is everything the Committee says, or rather we jump from one camp to another leaving all knowledge of our previous camp out of consciousness, and putting up barriers against its re-entry. Therefore I tentatively tried the effect of one rather unselected paragraph of the Report upon a mature, homosexual and fairly intelligent, man patient. I told him to interrupt me with any remark that he felt like making. Rather arbitrarily I chose paragraph 196: "From whichever of the foregoing points of view it may be regarded, treatment itself will vary through a wide range, if only to match the diversity of individual personalities." (At this point the patient expostulated sarcastically: "*Sic*.") "It is important to remember that 'treatment' need not necessarily, or even often, imply any active steps to be taken by a physician or by a psychiatrist. Often it will be desirable that various methods of treatment should be applied simultaneously, bringing into service a combination of many helpers."

At this point the patient said: "Combination of many helpers! Why not just *love?* That is what everybody wants . . ."

The paragraph flowed on "And in this work there is a place for the clergyman, the psychiatric social worker, the probation officer and, it may be added, the adjusted homosexual, as well as for the doctor."

At this point the patient laughed and added: "Uncle Tom Cobley and all."* Later, where the term "successful results" is used, the patient remarked: "It is all lies, the only successful result is not being caught, and naturally one tells any lies to assist that."

Having been loosened up, this patient went on to say: "I wish they would set up a committee of homosexuals to say what they think of *heterosexuality*. I will tell you this much: most of us think it is absolutely disgusting. We cannot understand

* Traditional Devonshire ballad: "Widecombe Fair."

why anybody wants to behave like that. Perhaps it would be a good thing if the penalties they inflict on us were inflicted on them instead!"

These remarks are of course in keeping with the attitude that the only important thing is not to be caught. But if we compromise between the two points of view, perhaps we could wash them both out and suggest that the law should, as it generally attempts to do (I hope), be concerned merely with the protection of the public against unwanted interference.

I think it may be said for the Wolfenden Committee that had their terms of reference been limited to a consideration of the law and practice relating to homosexual offences, they may have had at least some firm ground to stand on, and may not have done so badly. It seems to me that it has been the additional and perhaps unjustified matter of considering the *treatment* of homosexual offenders that has got them embroiled into very complicated matter far out of their depth. In fact, it has forced them to encroach upon the province of a science of which they knew nothing.

More than this, it has stimulated and to some extent revealed to us the enormous defensive construction built up against the repressed bogies in the mind—not a suitable basis for dispassionate or scientific research. The first research, as is the case in every individual analysis, has to be directed against this defensive construction, for it is only from beneath this that the unconscious phantasies which are the source of all our behaviours and beliefs, can be admitted to consciousness. Perhaps this Report is a good lesson in the futility of trying to unravel and assess psychological phenomena without first removing the obstacles to understanding their meaning.

The Wolfenden Committee evidently preferred to listen

to policemen as a basis on which to judge not only homosexual crimes but homosexuality. As regards their assignment relating to crime there is some justification, but to my mind crime is crime and has not necessarily anything to do with homosexuality. We cannot be too clear in our minds in distinguishing between crime and psychopathology. Crime involves violation of other people's freedom and liberty (the sort of thing we tend to do to homosexuals just because they are homosexuals). Crime has not necessarily anything to do with homosexuality, but operates in every field of human activity. It would seem, though, that we tend to lose our reason when it comes to homosexuality, on account of our emotionally overcharged repressed conflicts. This comes out clearly in the disproportionate severity of the legal penalties.

When it comes to the second assignment of the Committee, namely the practice relating to "the treatment of persons convicted of such [homosexual] offences," I would suggest that the Committee would have done better to read Freud than to listen to policemen. Had they done so they might have come across the following letter which, written in the 1930's, reveals far greater enlightenment than anything which they have to offer us. It was sent to a despairing mother in America, who had written to Freud to ask advice about her son. This is the first paragraph:

"I gather from your letter that your son is a homosexual. I am most impressed by the fact that you do not mention this term yourself in your information about him. May I question you, why you avoid it? Homosexuality is assuredly no advantage, but it is nothing to be ashamed of, no vice, no degradation, it cannot be classified as an illness; we consider it to be a variation of the sexual function produced by a certain arrest of sexual development. Many highly respected individuals of ancient and modern times have been homosexuals, several of the greatest men among them (Plato, Michaelangelo, Leonardo da Vinci, etc.). It is a great injustice to persecute homosexuality as a crime, and cruelty too . . ."

It strikes one that had the Wolfenden Committee read Freud, they might have saved themselves three years of perplexity and trouble and the nation £8,046 (the estimated cost of preparing the Report) . . . and what is of course more important than any of this, arrived at an enlightened conclusion.